CLIMATE AND MAN

From the Ice Ages
to the Global Greenhouse

CLIMATE AND MAN

From the Ice Ages
to the Global Greenhouse

FRED PEARCE

VISION BOOKS in association with LWT

First published in Britain in 1989 by
VISION BOOKS, The Forum, 74–80 Camden Street
London NW1 0EG

BRITISH LIBRARY CATALOGUING PUBLICATION DATA

Pearce, Fred
Climate and Man

ISBN 1 872218

Printed and bound in Great Britain by
Butler & Tanner Ltd, Frome and London

Contents

Acknowledgements

Thanks are due to the production team of CLIMATE AND MAN, particularly the series consultant, Professor Tom Wigley, Producer/Director Mark Redhead; Director, Ralph Jones; Associate Producer, Claire Odgers; Researcher, Louise Joll and the Production Manager, Faye Dimdore.

CLIMATE AND MAN

INTRODUCTION

Biospheres I and II

In a giant geodesic greenhouse near Tucson, in the Arizona desert, scientists are building a miniature Earth. Sometime in 1990, four men and four women will step inside. They will stay there for two years, completely sealed off from the outside world. The only things to enter will be sunlight and radio waves bringing the output of local TV and radio stations. But inside, there will be some 4000 species of insects, animals and plants, each playing a part in seven different miniature ecosystems that mimic the outside world. The greenhouse, which covers about one hectare of land, will contain a desert, grassland, a swamp, a coral reef and a tropical rainforest. These ecosystems will help to recycle heat, water and air, as well as provide food and energy.

The high-tech greenhouse is called Biosphere II. (Its designers say that Biosphere I is the Earth.) It is being built according to the geodesic principles of the visionary designer Buckminster Fuller. Its chief engineer, Peter Pearce, is one of Fuller's protégés from the 1970s. Biosphere II will cost some £20 million, a bill paid by an oil millionaire from Houston called Edward Bass, the brother of Robert Bass who owns Disneyworld in California. But this is no outsize fantasy. It is a piece of deadly serious scientific endeavour. The designers hope that their combined architectural and biological ingenuity will be good enough to feed and sustain the eight human inhabitants and to prevent their water becoming contaminated or their air polluted.

Biosphere II is a latterday ark. The immediate purpose of the project is to design a self-contained life-support system that would enable a future mission by astronauts to Mars to survive on the planet without constantly being resupplied from Earth. Such research could one day allow large numbers of humans to colonise other planets, if our own home becomes too overcrowded or if humans succeed in destroying the Earth's own natural life-support systems. Alternatively, the science to be done inside Biosphere II could provide vital clues to how our planet works. As we grab from nature the controls of spaceship Earth, it may help us draw up a first draft of an operating manual for our planet. If that proves a forlorn hope then maybe, as the oceans and atmosphere become more polluted, we will all one day have to live our lives inside individual biospheres.

The atmosphere of Biosphere II will contain higher levels of carbon dioxide than are currently found on Biosphere I. This will allow the greenhouse's inmates to

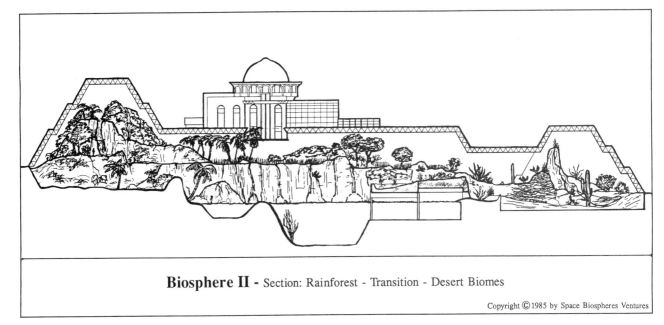

Biosphere II - Section: Rainforest - Transition - Desert Biomes

Home from home: Biosphere II will mimic our world (known to biospherians as biosphere I).

assess whether plants such as rice that will be cultivated inside can grow faster, providing hard evidence about whether our planet, warming under the influence of the greenhouse effect, might also be a more agriculturally productive world in the decades to come.

The biospherians will be an international bunch. The shortlist includes people from Mexico, the USA, Britain, West Germany, Belgium, Australia and France. Socially, says one candidate, Margaret Augustine, 'this is a tremendous opportunity to model a future international base on the moon or Mars.' To while away their days, the biospherians will have a library and astronomical observatory, workshops and laboratories. But they must also tend the fish, chickens and pygmy sheep and goats on the biosphere's farm, which will provide much of their food.

Carl Hodges, another biospherian, is excited by the prospect of testing new forms of agriculture, such as seawater irrigation. 'There are 30 000 kilometres of desert sea coasts in the world,' he says. 'If we could irrigate those with seawater, have a plant that could grow in seawater, we could produce food and have desirable places for people to live. We have gone all over the world to find plants that will grow in seawater. One we are really excited about. We call it SOS7. It gives us a little seed that has no salt in it but is about 30 per cent oil, a very high quality vegetable oil that produces a meal like soya bean.'

For some scientists, this futuristic talk is a high-tech nightmare. Pat Zimmerman, a biologist from the USA's National Center for Atmospheric Research, works on termite mounds, a kind of insect biosphere, and investigates how they may be contributing to the greenhouse effect by pumping increasing amounts of methane into the air. He takes a dim view of Biosphere II. 'The fundamental problem,' he says, 'is that, as always, humans seem to have the arrogance to think that they can duplicate nature in a test tube. We don't understand the processes well enough to do it.' If Zimmerman is right we can expect to see the biospherians scurrying from their greenhouse soon after entry, choking from acid fumes, or with some disease having wiped out their food supply. Zimmerman predicts much the same fate for the Earth itself.

Ghillean Prance, the director of Kew Botanical Gardens in England, is a biologist with a special interest in the tropical rainforests and he is one of the scientific advisers for the Biosphere II programme. He is not so interested in missions to Mars, but sees the project as real science, aimed at increasing our understanding of the processes that run the Earth. 'I think it's a fascinating experiment,' he says. 'We can learn a great deal about the biosphere in which we live. I'm interested because of what I can learn about the way the rainforest works and about the regeneration of rainforest.'

The rainforests of Biosphere I are big and unwieldy, remote and full of dangerous creatures. And measuring the gases that they give off into the atmosphere is all but impossible. By comparison, measuring the rainforest in Biosphere II is easy. 'We have monitors all over the rainforest in Biosphere II that will tell us what is going on, what gases are being given off by the trees, whether they are reaching toxic levels at any time, how much carbon dioxide is coming into the atmosphere, what changes are taking place in the acidity of the soil. These are wonderful data for addressing the problems of deforestation. I think the biospherians' dream is a good dream and an exciting one,' says Prance.

Stephen Schneider, one of Zimmerman's colleagues at the NCAR, is unmoved both by the science and by the vision of building our own surrogate world. He believes that we know enough about what we are doing wrong that is destroying our world. High-tech extravaganzas such as Biosphere II are a distraction. He wants to get on with the less glamorous business of saving our planet and its inhabitants rather than developing the technology to rebuild it somewhere else in the universe.

'There are always people who will say that the Earth is hopeless and we really need to have another world in space. Biosphere II is an example. If people want to go out and try founding space colonies, they're welcome to it. But there isn't a very large fraction of the people on Earth who are going to be able to ship out there. I for one am not the explorer type and I don't think I'd want to go into a very small ecologically self-sustained unit that could easily collapse with one bad disease that you hadn't planned for. If we are really going to do something for the bulk of humanity, the major effort has to be on curing problems at home and we already know how to do it. It's not that we have to invent new things. What we have to invent is the political will to make the investments and the hard choices to make our planet environmentally sustainable. It can be done. We have to choose to do it.'

All this may be true. But Biosphere II stands as a powerful metaphor. Humans have invented Biosphere II, but Biosphere I becomes every day more our invention and we are now, for practical purposes, in control of it. We must learn how to manage it, sustain its soils, preserve its oceans and prevent its atmosphere, our weather, from raining destruction on us. It is now 40 years since Fairfield Osborn, one of the earliest portenders of ecological doom, wrote *Our Plundered Planet*, in which he said: 'It is man's earth now. One wonders what obligations may accompany this infinite possession.' Mankind's most important task at the end of the twentieth century is to uncover what those obligations are. Biosphere II, for all the ballyhoo, may provide part of the answer.

This book is both about our weather and about how humans are interfering with Biosphere I. The two are inextricably entwined. Part One, called 'The Goldilocks Planet', explores how our planet and its atmosphere came into being and why our climate is the way it is. It looks at ice ages, sun spots and the 'natural' greenhouse effect, which stops our world from being as cold and barren as Mars. And it takes the temperature of the planet today, looking at evidence that in recent decades our world has warmed. Are such events as the drought of 1988 in the USA and Hurricane Gilbert, the most intense tropical storm for a century, which occurred in the same year, the first signs of a change in our weather?

The second, 'A Change in the Weather', looks at the weather forecasters and how the weather and its prediction can alter the course of history. It looks at the deliberate manipulation of the weather—by cloud seeding, for instance—and at inadvertent changes—heat islands over cities and the loss of rain as forests are cut down. It asks: are humans responsible for the desiccation of Africa? And it looks too at the consequences of destroying tropical rainforests for the planet.

The third part—'Models of the Future'—investigates the 'greenhouse gases' such as carbon dioxide and methane that are set to warm our world, at the computer models designed to predict the changes. It offers a glimpse into the future—a world of rising tides consuming whole nations, of rich farmland turning to dust and of hundreds of millions of 'ecological refugees' looking for new homes. And it asks the question: could Britain conceivably benefit from this, with warmer weather bringing bumper crops?

The final part offers a 'Prognosis for the Planet'. Can we kick the coal habit? Will Britain become a haven for wind power, with a wind turbine in every back yard? Must we abandon our cars and dim the lights in a bid for energy efficiency? Is nuclear power the solution? There is an analysis of the likely increase in tensions between the rich developed world (which has created most of the planet's problems) and the poor world, which may be burdened with implementing many of the solutions if it wishes to become rich too. How can the international community bring fairness to a strategy for saving our planet? Finally, and perhaps most importantly of all, the question is asked: can the task be done? In the final pages, the optimists and pessimists battle it out.

PART ONE

The Goldilocks Planet

CHAPTER 1

The primeval greenhouse

Nobody knows quite how our world began, but the universe was already quite old when it happened. Some 10 billion years had probably passed since the Big Bang when the Earth was formed, a semi-molten volcanic ball flying through space. Perhaps Earth was made from the slow accretion of tiny fragments of matter crashing into each other across the vast chaos of the universe. Or perhaps it emerged from an explosion of the sun. Whatever the truth, some 5 billion years ago, the Earth was part of the cosmos and had settled into an orbit round the sun. And by 4 billion years ago its surface had solidified and an atmosphere had formed around it. It was ready for life to begin its odyssey from the most primitive forms to *homo sapiens*.

During the twentieth century humans have become overwhelmingly the dominant force on the planet, bringing untold benefits to themselves. But now, in the late 1980s, we have become aware that this tantalising power brings with it terrifying responsibilities. We have begun to listen to the warnings of scientists who are convinced that humanity has gained such control over the Earth that we threaten the life-support systems of the planet. A world that has been a benign host to myriad forms of life for some 4 billion years is being disfigured and could be made barren within a few decades.

Remarkably, this new concern is being reflected by politicians, including British politicians. If one event encapsulated this sudden excursion by Whitehall and Westminster into the worlds of ecology and atmospheric chemistry during 1989, it occurred on 26 April, when the Prime Minister, Margaret Thatcher, called in an array of prominent scientists from Britain and around the world to Downing Street to explain their concerns to a collection of her Cabinet ministers and top officials. Heading the agenda was the 'greenhouse effect' by which pollution, mostly from burning coal and oil, is beginning to warm the atmosphere at an unprecedented rate, bringing the threat of massive disruption to weather systems, widespread flooding, the death of forests and crops and the spread of deserts. Ultimately it could threaten the habitability of the planet itself.

Leading the Downing Street discussions was Tom Wigley, a former weather forecaster from Adelaide in South Australia who is now the director of the Climatic Research Unit, a world-famous laboratory attached to the University of East Anglia. His researchers have charted the warming of the planet over the past century and calculated the likely effects. Wigley believes that part of our understanding of the future lies in events that occurred at the dawn of our planet. It was then that the greenhouse effect, the great regulator of temperature on our planet, began to operate.

'Let me start 4 billion years ago,' he says, 'when the world was without life and there were no continents. . . . At that time we know that the sun was much less bright than it is today and yet there was ocean rather than ice. There may have been a large ocean covering the whole earth. One reason is that there was a lot of carbon dioxide in the atmosphere.'

Carbon dioxide, then as now, was the most important gas involved in the greenhouse effect. It has always been present in our atmosphere, trapping the sun's heat, absorbing it and preventing it from escaping back into space. In the days when our sun was young and relatively weak, the amount of carbon dioxide in the Earth's atmosphere was many times higher than today. Since then, the story of our atmosphere has been one of slowly declining amounts of carbon dioxide, keeping the temperature of the surface of the Earth reasonably constant as the sun has gained in strength. There have been fluctuations, of course. Indeed, if anything, despite the strengthening sun, our world is currently cooler than in past aeons. Around 100 million years ago, when dinosaurs roamed the Earth, says Wigley, 'the climate was very much warmer than today. There was probably no ice at all on the Earth's surface.' It is only in the past 3 million years or so that ice caps have formed over the poles, periodically reaching down to cover much of the planet during the ice ages. Levels of carbon dioxide reflect this, being much lower during the ice ages.

The history of life on our planet is not, as many suppose, one of seamless progress, of Darwinian evolution turning out ever better beings that inevitably take over from their more primitive forebears. Usually things happen in lurches, with some catastrophe paving the way for change. We mammals pride ourselves on our superiority over the lumbering dinosaurs that ruled the Earth before us. But without a great catastrophe that wiped out the dinosaurs 65 million years ago, they could still be in charge today.

That catastrophe, in which perhaps a half of all the world's species died out, was probably caused by the arrival of a giant meteorite that blasted into our planet, sending climates haywire. Something similar may have happened to establish the dinosaurs as top dogs perhaps 250 million years ago. Then, three-quarters of all the planet's species died out. Nobody knows why. Perhaps it was a meteorite. But perhaps it was a natural climatic event. It was a time when all the land masses on the planet had come together to form one giant continent called Pangaea. As this happened, climates probably became very turbulent. Monsoons were stronger around the coast of the giant continent, with tempestuous winds. But inland, there was one vast desert, extremely hot in the tropics but very cold at the poles. The planet was, we know, rather warmer then than today. One estimate is that it was around 5°C warmer, disturbingly similar to the kind of temperature we expect on

Earth in some 50 years' time. Will such temperatures trigger a similar catastrophe? Nobody knows, but the lessons from the past is that catastrophes are a more important part of the history of our planet than we have traditionally thought.

One researcher, John Kutzbach from the University of Wisconsin, identifies five great extinctions in the past and wonders if we might be on the verge of a sixth. Certainly, he says, 'some ecologists estimate that the destruction of tropical rainforests, along with other habitats, may produce extinction rates over the next century that will rival the five great extinctions of the past. This is one list of the top six that we don't need to join.'

Not too hot, not too cold

While Wigley and his investigators from East Anglia have briefed British politicians with their dire predictions, Stephen Schneider, one of a new generation of American scientists who have dedicated their lives to working on the greenhouse effect, has been doing the same in America. Schneider explains that we need the natural greenhouse effect, our comforting carbon dioxide blanket, in order to survive. 'If there was no such thing as a greenhouse effect, then it would be very hard for me, as a living being, to have this conversation because it has made the earth about 33° warmer than it otherwise would have been. In that sense the greenhouse effect is our friend. That's the good news. The bad news is that we're modifying the assembly of greenhouse gases in the air so rapidly that the 33° of nice warming that we're used to could become 35° or maybe even 40°, and it might happen in 100 years. That's the part of the greenhouse effect that isn't friendly, that we have to worry about.'

Scientists compare the Earth with Mars and Venus, its nearest neighbours among the planets that revolve around the sun. For many decades, researchers have wondered why there is life on Earth when its neighbours appear to be dead. They call the Earth 'the Goldilocks planet' after the story of Goldilocks and the three bears. Goldilocks—that is, life—developed here because Earth is not too hot (like Venus), not too cold (like Mars), but just right. This happy state of affairs arises partly because the Earth is at roughly the right distance from the sun. But it is increasingly clear that the greenhouse effect is a key factor. Without carbon dioxide to keep us warm, the Earth would be cold and inhospitable, and in the days when the sun was cooler life would certainly have been impossible. On Venus, the atmosphere is boiling with a constant temperature of some 400°C. The air there is made up almost entirely of carbon dioxide. Scientists call this a runaway greenhouse effect. Mars on the other hand has a very thin atmosphere containing few gases of any sort. There is no greenhouse blanket and the planet is today too cold for life. Some say that Mars was once much warmer, with running water and perhaps primitive life. If so, we don't know what went wrong. But whatever it was, the growing strength of the sun could not compensate.

Despite failures elsewhere in the solar system, the Earth has somehow evolved a system to maintain its atmosphere for 4 billion years at temperatures that suit life forms. Some people call this system a 'global thermostat'. The world may have been some 5° warmer than today when the Pangaea was at its height 250 million years ago. It may have been 5° colder than today at the height of the last (and seemingly most intense) ice age. But by comparison with the extremes suffered on Mars and Venus, the changes appear small and evidence of some benign force at work. If there is a global thermostat, three questions arise. How exactly does it work? What controls it? And have we broken it? On the answers to those questions may hang the future of life, certainly human life, on the Earth.

Not too hot like Venus (top left), not too cold like Mars (top right), the Earth (above) is just right, says Stephen Schneider of the National Center for Atmospheric Research, Boulder, Colorado.

CHAPTER 2

Ice and the wobbly planet

For several million years now, the Earth has plunged every 100 000 years or so into an ice age during which ice sheets cover much of the planet. Scientists remain perplexed about what caused this sequence of ice ages to begin, since fossils from earlier times show no evidence of ice. And debate continues about how and why the ice ages regularly appear. Explanations range from wobbles in the Earth's orbit round the sun to changes in winds caused by the rise of mountain chains. But central to much of the debate is the influence of carbon dioxide and the greenhouse effect. We need to know why ice ages happen because humans may already be tampering with the mechanisms that cause them. And despite the warming we are inflicting on the planet, the next natural ice age could be less than 1000 years away.

Tom Wigley puts the start of the era of the ice ages at about 3 million years ago. It was, he says, 'a rather remarkable change' in the history of the planet. 'Ice started to appear in high latitudes and every 100 000 years or so it advanced right down over the British Isles.'

The most recent ice age was at its coldest 20 000 years ago. It began to relent about 15 000 years ago, after which the world warmed rapidly, reaching its hottest perhaps 6000 years ago. The Thames Valley, which had recently formed the southern edge of the Arctic ice cap, was by then populated by lions. Hippopotamuses roamed the Scottish borders. After that time, the slow slide into the next ice age began, only to be reversed by human activity in the past century.

The average temperature round the world is today roughly 4°C warmer than at the coldest phase of the most recent ice age. But within 50 years it is likely to be 8° or 9° warmer, quite enough for hippopotamuses to return to Britain. Indeed, investigators such as Wigley believe that by 2050 the world will be warmer than for at least 200 000 years, and perhaps as warm as when the dinosaurs ruled.

Ice ages seem to coincide with wobbles in the rotation of the Earth round the sun. The wobbles were first described in detail in the 1920s by Milutin Milankovitch, a Serbian mathematician. There are a number of separate wobbles, each lasting tens of thousands of years. But the most important is a shift in the angle of the Earth's rotation. Anybody with a globe will know that the Earth revolves on its axis at an angle to the sun. This gives us our seasons, since it causes the sun to be

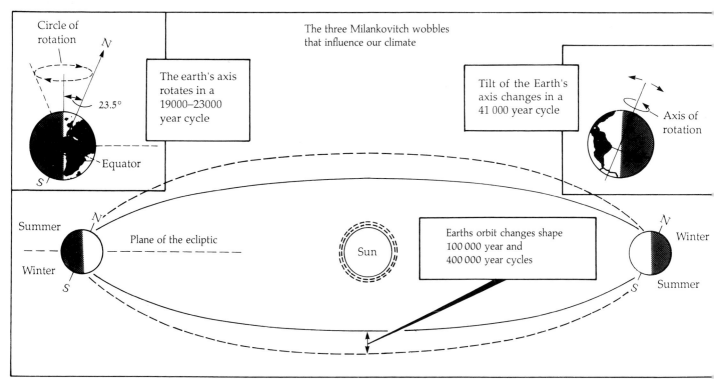

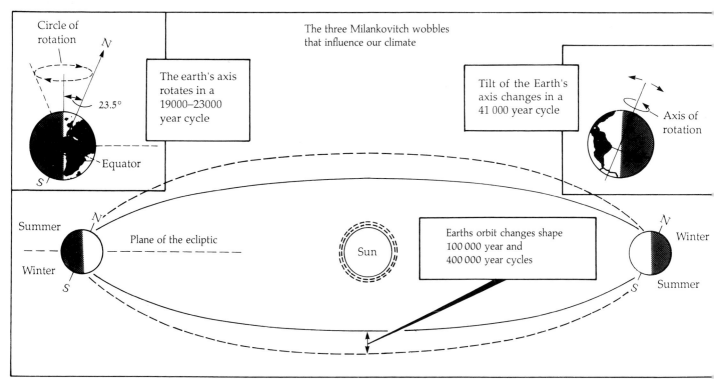

Circle of rotation

N

23.5°

Equator

S

The earth's axis rotates in a 19000–23000 year cycle

The three Milankovitch wobbles that influence our climate

Tilt of the Earth's axis changes in a 41 000 year cycle

Axis of rotation

Summer

Winter

N

S

Plane of the ecliptic

Sun

Earths orbit changes shape 100 000 year and 400 000 year cycles

N

Winter

S

Summer

Credit: New Scientist

overhead, and so at its hottest, at different places at different times of the year. But over thousands of years, this angle of rotation changes as the Earth wobbles like a large slow-moving top.

One effect of this wobble is to vary the intensity of the seasons. As Wigley points out, 'These orbital variations don't alter the total amount of radiation that the Earth receives each year. What they do change is the distribution of that radiation, both spatially and seasonally.'

So, 6000–9000 years ago, when the world was at its hottest, there was a lot more sun reaching us in summer, but a lot less in winter. At the depths of the ice ages, the opposite was the case. The northern hemisphere was receiving less radiation from the sunlight in summer than today, but more in winter. This small change had a major effect on the ice cap around the Arctic. According to Bill Ruddiman from the Lamont–Doherty Geological Observatory at Columbia University in New York, the man who developed many of these ideas, the shift in the intensity of the seasons acts as a 'pacemaker for the ice ages'.

It works like this. Any ice cap, such as those over the Antarctic and the Arctic today, spreads towards warmer latitudes in winter and retreats in summer. A series of warm summers will reduce the average size of the cap, while a run of cold winters will make it grow. But for some reason, the summer temperatures seem to be more important. When summers are cooler than normal in the northern hemisphere, the Arctic ice cap will advance further south each year until eventually it forms vast masses of ice more than a kilometre thick, covering huge areas of Asia, Europe and North America.

The severity of this change is quite surprising. The changes in the sun's heat

Pack ice covered Britain during the last ice age, but within 10,000 years hippos wallowed in the River Thames (right) and lions prowled the banks.

Bill Ruddiman of Columbia University, New York, believes that the rise of the Rocky Mountains in America triggered the onset of the ice ages.

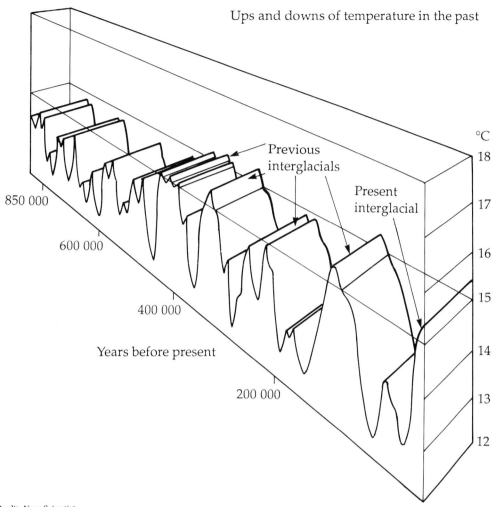

Ups and downs of temperature in the past

Credit: New Scientist

the planet's reflectivity and meandering winds is involved in the ice ages. That something else is the greenhouse effect.

It turns out that the amount of carbon dioxide in the atmosphere is reduced during ice ages – just when it would be handy for amounts of the gas to increase in order to keep the planet warm. The ice bubbles reveal that temperatures rise and fall almost exactly as the amount of the carbon dioxide in the air rises and falls, except (most tantalisingly of all) that the changes in carbon dioxide happen slightly after the Milankovitch wobbles but slightly before the changes in the amount of ice. This means that the planetary wobbles must cause the changes in carbon dioxide and that together they influence the size of the ice caps. All three then act together to swing the planet into and out of ice ages.

Nobody is certain why tiny changes in the amount of sunlight reaching our in concert should trigger this change in the greenhouse effect. Most guess that it has something to do with the oceans. Plankton in the oceans are the leading candidates. They absorb carbon dioxide and despatch it to the ocean depths, a process called the 'biological pump'.

If plankton respond to a slight cooling in the planet by reproducing faster and sucking more carbon dioxide out of the air, then they could drag the world into an ice age. And if they responded to a slight warming by slowing their absorption, that would swiftly warm our world and end an ice age.

CHAPTER 3

Children of the forest

Climate has been critical to virtually every stage of human evolution, from the emergence of the first human-like creatures that evolved from apes, through to the origin and development of our own species, *homo sapiens*. Without the changing wetness of the tropics and the cycles of the ice ages, some very different creatures from us could be lording it over the planet.

Human-like creatures, known to archaeologists as hominids, first appeared on Earth perhaps 8 million years ago in Africa. It was then that hominids became recognisably different from apes. Robert Foley, of the Department of Biological Anthropology at Cambridge, says, 'The environment at that time seemed to be very interesting.' In the years before hominids emerged, tropical Africa was heavily forested. 'You had these great stretches of rainforest, but from about 10 million years ago, the forests became fragmented. We see the expansion of drier environments, of more grassland. The appearance of hominids seems to coincide with the change,' Not only that, the changes that hominids underwent as they developed mirror the challenges presented by the changing environment. 'One of the principal features of humans is that we are bipedal—we walk upright on two legs. This form of locomotion is particularly appropriate for living on the ground.' Hominids, in other words, came down out of the trees, either of their own accord or because the branches were becoming overpopulated with primates. And they adapted to living in the vast grassy plains that formed in Africa some 8 million years ago.

Bipeds cannot run fast, like cheetahs, say, but they can run for long distances. 'Hominids were naturally selected for jogging,' says Foley. And that too fits the needs of the grasslands. In the forest everything that the apes needed was close at hand, but in the grasslands the resources needed to survive were more widely distributed. These early hominids would have had to travel much further to find sufficient food, whether animal or vegetable.

The first anthropologists, Europeans of around a century ago, supposed that the cradle of civilisation would be Europe—preferably Britain—and that is where they looked for fossils. The great fossil hoax, Piltdown Man, was 'uncovered' in Sussex in 1912. But it is now clear that the real cradle of virtually every phase of human evolution is tropical Africa.

The first hominids emerged there as the forests thinned. Among these early inhabitants of the African plains was the highly successful *Australopithecus*, which

Australopithecus (above left) ruled the African plains for a million years, Neanderthal man (above) conquered Europe, but modern man (*homo sapiens*) had colonised the world, including Australia (left) around 40,000 years ago.

survived in various forms for several million years. Then, around a million years ago, one of those forms spawned *homo erectus*. The birthplace was central Africa. *Homo erectus* was the first hominid to begin to look like a modern human, with an enlarged brain and a fully upright gait. *Homo erectus* also became probably the first hominid to leave Africa. Members of this species went to both Europe and Asia, where archaeologists have found remnants of various forms of *homo erectus*, known as Java Man and Peking Man. *Homo erectus* used stone tools extensively and Peking Man at least had discovered fire, which was probably essential for life away from the tropics.

The date of the arrival of modern man, *homo sapiens*, is disputed. Some anthropologists say that human skulls dating from 250 000 years ago and found at Swanscombe in England are the remains of *homo sapiens*. But the large brains of truly modern man are more recent. Foley says that *homo sapiens* first emerged, again from Africa, around 100 000 years ago. From there, he began to migrate perhaps as recently as 40 000 years ago, spreading right round the world and seeing off other related species of hominids. Then, around 10 000 years ago, as the last ice age abated, he began to take up cultivating crops and domesticating animals, and then building cities. Genetic evolution had given way to an even more potent change: social evolution.

One interesting question is what caused *homo erectus* and, later, *homo sapiens* to leave tropical Africa and conquer the world. The answer, says Foley, is opportunity. The earliest hominids didn't have very large brains; their technology was very simple and in terms of diet they were probably very similar to the apes. They were largely collecting fruit and vegetables and maybe scavenging for meat. What happened with *homo erectus*, the first hominid to get out of Africa, is that his diet changed. *Homo erectus* was the first primate to become a meat eater, a hunter. 'The interesting thing is that animals dependent on meat seem to be much more tolerant of differences in habitat than plant specialists. It could well be that, having acquired this new characteristic, humans were able to tolerate new environments. I suspect that might be the breakthrough,' says Foley. So *homo erectus* was suddenly able to roam into the cool woodlands of Europe and the plains of Asia, chasing whatever animals crossed his path, rather than puzzling over which of a vast range of unfamiliar plants might be edible.

For millions of years, the Earth's climate has been dominated by the swings into and out of ice ages. There may have been up to 20 complete cycles within the past 2 million years. So all the time that humans have been evolving and dispersing from Africa, there have been wild changes in climate. Such changes are bound to have had an important effect on where humans have moved.

Ironically, the ice ages may have encouraged human migrations into colder latitudes as much as they restricted them. This is because ice ages locked up large amounts of the planet's water in huge ice sheets, and so lowered sea levels by at least 100 metres. Land bridges formed between the continents and between continents and islands. Humans could cross from the old to the new world via the dried-up bed of the Bering Sea between Alaska and eastern Siberia. Not all these migrations would have been successful. The first incursions into North America, more than 30 000 years ago, probably failed. Human endeavour has had its setbacks as well as its successes, and some early communities in the north would undoubtedly have frozen to death. The picture that emerges is one of pulses of humans spreading out from Africa across the world and from time to time being forced back or dying out.

What also emerges is that each succeeding wave seems to have been more successful than the last. One of the most interesting episodes was the arrival of the Neanderthals. They may have been large bullish individuals, but they have suffered an unduly bad press. They were the innovators and thinkers of their day and, says Foley, 'specialists at living in cold conditions'. Indeed from the fossil evidence they appear to have been a rare, perhaps unique, example of a successful type of humanity that developed in Europe rather than Africa. 'Neanderthals are only found in Europe,' he says, 'spreading down into the Middle East and across a little into central Asia.' They were at their height of dominance during the last glaciation, from 70 000 years ago to around 30 000 years ago.

The physical adaptation of Neanderthals to cold climate is seen in their large noses, which were capable of warming the air before it reached the bronchial passages, and their short limbs, which would have conserved body heat by minimising surface areas of their skin. The Neanderthals survived for around 100 000 years, 'More than we have managed so far,' as Foley points out. 'I think they were very successful. But in the end they became extinct.'

They gave way, in a manner that remains mysterious, to *homo sapiens*, who trekked out of Africa to the colder climates of the north, including Europe, around 40 000 years ago. To arrive from the tropics at the height of the ice age and completely displace an established species well adapted to cold climates suggested that *homo sapiens* must have been something special. And having displaced the Neanderthals they lived on in Europe and elsewhere in the frozen north to survive the coldest period known throughout geological history, around 18 000 years ago in the final stages of the last ice age.

'How they were able to survive where the Neanderthals had failed is one of the great mysteries,' agrees Foley. 'One can look perhaps at greater technological skills.' Perhaps they were able to travel further in search of food. Perhaps they invented sleds. 'One of the things technology does is to enable us to save time—and time is very important in high latitudes.' Where the winters were long and hard, humans had to use the short summers to gather the food and materials that they needed to survive. Perhaps social organisation also played a part. If they lived in larger groups that were socially more cohesive they would have stood a better chance of surviving in an extreme climate. 'High latitudes,' says Foley, 'require planning, organisation and scheduling of behaviour, and technology tends to reflect that in terms of its complexity.' So, while modern humans may be, genetically speaking, the children of the tropics, in social terms they are perhaps children of the ice. We have the sweat glands and hairless bodies of a species adapted to the tropics. But we have the social organisation that fits us for civilisation in a cold climate.

For Foley it is extraordinarily exciting to realise that our own species is so young, having been on the earth for no more than 100 000 years. 'It means that many of the things that are happening today and that have been happening over the past 30 000 years are in a sense part of the appearance of *homo sapiens*. We are still evolving, we are still changing very rapidly.'

The mark of that evolution is still seen strongly in central Africa where the genetic diversity of the local population is higher than in places where colonisation by humans has come later, much as the species diversity is greatest in the core areas of the great tropical rainforests. That, he suggests, also means that any rival to our ascendancy would be likely to come from that region.

Homo sapiens appears to have been the first species of hominid to spread right across the planet. Antarctica was the only environment to elude him until it was settled by scientists in the present century. *Homo sapiens* reached Australia 40 000 years ago, the first land mammals to arrive for millions of years. But he conquered the Americas, after several false starts, perhaps only 12 000 years ago when big game hunters from Siberia made the crossing and established themselves on the prairies. The pickings were rich, with bison with horn spreads of 2 metres and a vast beaver-like creature called castoroides, as well as lion-sized cats, camels, horses and mammoths. Within a thousand years, many of the animals had been made extinct by the hunters.

The earlier hominids were tightly restricted by their environment, says Foley. 'Once we get modern humans, however, we have something entirely different, a species which spreads very rapidly, in parts of Europe almost explosively.'

Foley believes that flexibility has been the key to our success. 'And that relates perhaps to the nature of our brain and its very large size, allowing us to consider options for behaviour and to make decisions about how to deal with things, and how to organise people to achieve particular goals.' So, having come from the tropics to survive in the worst ice age ever, we are perhaps uniquely able to respond and adapt to the climatic change that we now appear about to foist on our planet. In the same way 40 000 years ago the Neanderthals must have appeared uniquely equipped to survive the ice age—yet upstarts from the tropics saw them off on their own territory. 'When we look at modern humans and talk about the possibility of our own extinction,' says Foley, 'the question that arises is whether it is going to be due to changing climates or to a new type of humanoid or even a new animal of some sort arriving. I think the answer to that is that we have no idea.'

Dawn of civilisation

The end of the most recent ice age provided the opportunity for communities of *homo sapiens* to give birth to modern forms of civilisation, based on settled farmers supplying foods to towns and cities. But in other areas and for other peoples, about whom we know little, it was the end of an era. Sea levels throughout the ice age were 100 metres or more lower than today. Many of today's shallow seas would have been dry land then—and inhabited. But as the ice melted, sea levels rapidly rose.

'There is little doubt,' says Hubert Lamb, Wigley's predecessor as head of the Climatic Research Unit, 'that some of the densest populations of the world were then living along the edge of the sea—because that was the place where you could make salt ... primitive man's equivalent of the modern refrigerator for keeping food. Whether you're talking about Europe or Australia or the China Sea, when the sea level rose as rapidly as it did, there must have been great loss of life. The industrial sites, the salt-producing sites, had to be abandoned.' This could be the origin of the myth of Atlantis.

But the defeated do not make history, so the main story of the end of the ice is of human success. As the world warmed, people were swift to adapt to the new opportunities. The first city may have been Jericho, founded near the Dead Sea in modern Jordan around 10 000 years ago. By 6000 years ago, temperatures had reached their peak in modern times, perhaps 2° in warmer than today in summer, though no warmer in winter. At that time, a swathe of the world from the Mediterranean, east through the Fertile Crescent of modern Iraq and Iran, where the Tigris and Euphrates rivers flow, to the Indus Valley of northwest India, was inhabited by highly sophisticated agrarian civilisations.

Much of this cradle of civilisation is now dry and barren, inhabited by a few peasant farmers. There are a number of possible reasons for the demise. Many of the cultures became exhausted by war and strife. There is evidence that their fields slowly became poisoned by salt left there by water used to irrigate crops. But Reid Bryson from the University of Wisconsin, the author of a book called *Climates of Hunger*, sees the root cause as changing climates created by the planetary wobble that brought hot summers 6000 years ago.

'If we go back to the time when the big civilisations were developing, say 6000 years ago, there was a lot more rain,' he says. In those days, winter storms blew from the Mediterranean across the Middle East as far as the Tigris and Euphrates and even as far as northern India. Also, the hot summer weather accentuated the difference in temperature between land and sea, causing intense monsoons. As a result, deserts were rare. The Sahara filled with water and wildlife. And the Indian monsoon penetrated further inland than today, bringing summer rain to much of the Middle East. Together, these rain-bearing weather systems from west and east brought rain to the whole region, allowing 'a much larger area of arable land than at the present time'.

24

Well shaft in Mohenjo Daro. Irrigated fields covered Mesopotamia 5,000 years ago. Today, it is barren desert on which the Gulf War was fought during the 1980s.

It did not last. Today, says Bryson, 'if you fly southeast from Damascus in Syria you see modern farms for some distance, but for hundreds of miles beyond that you can see the ancient field patterns extending out into the desert.' Most of those fields are now abandoned. The patch of desert at the mouth of the Euphrates, where Iran and Iraq fought the Gulf War through the 1980s, was once the biggest grain exporting region in the world, much like the modern-day Midwest of the USA.

The halcyon days 'came to an end rather abruptly 3700 years ago', says Bryson, when the winds bearing winter rains from the Mediterranean ceased. At about the same time, the Indian monsoon weakened and began to penetrate less far inland. When it failed to reach the Indus Valley, that civilisation also succumbed. The Indian monsoon failed altogether for about 700 years, says Bryson. 'A lot of civilisations disappeared during that time.'

Bryson believes that there is strong evidence from archaeological remains and climatic data to show that climate changes have caused the demise of many civilisations. 'If one looks at the best records we have of climate century by century for the past 10 000 years or so, we find that there are preferred times of rapid climatic change. If we compare those with a statistical analysis of when cultures came and went (there are 3000 dated cultures), we find that there are globally preferred times and that there is strong preference for times of rapid climatic change.' This is not surprising, he says. 'After all, climate provides the economic base for practically everybody on earth.'

So when are these key moments in history? Bryson offers seven: 5000 years ago, 3500 years ago, about 900 BC and AD 400, 900, 1200 and 1550–1600. 'If you look round you'll find that important things were happening at those times everywhere in the world.'

CHAPTER 4

Little ice ages

As the great adventures of the Middle East failed, the chalice of civilisation was handed to people living in wetter lands to the west and north, first Greece and Rome, then northern Europe. The influence of the northern Europeans stretched far and wide as time went on. But it too was constrained by the vagaries of climate, most notably by a phenomenon known as the little ice age which lasted for around 600 years and began between AD 1000 and AD 1200. Once the little ice age was seen as a local curiosity, the reason, for instance, why the River Thames iced over each winter allowing fairs to be held on it many years during the seventeenth century. The reason, perhaps, why Brueghel painted so many winter scenes. Now, partly due to the pioneering work of Hubert Lamb, it is recognised as a major climatic event coming at the end of several centuries of warm weather, with worldwide repercussions for civilisation.

From the eleventh and twelfth centuries, says Lamb, 'the glaciers started to grow, and by fits and starts the climate became a lot more unpleasant from most people's point of view, and especially in northern countries.' The cold came and went several times. The Thames first froze over a wide area in the winter of 1269–70, and froze every few decades thereafter for more than four centuries, with a gap only during a warm phase from 1434 to 1540. From 1440 to 1540, England was mild enough for cherries to be cultivated high in the Durham hills.

The little ice age was at its most intense in Europe in the seventeenth century. The glaciers of the Alps and Iceland reached their greatest extents in mid-century. And the first frost fair was held on the Thames Ice in 1607–08. Others followed, with two in the 1680s at the very height of the little ice age. (The Thames last froze in 1813–14.)

One of the peoples to suffer most from the little ice age were the Vikings, the Norse raiders who some 900 years ago had extended their empire from Russia and Constantinople (Istanbul) in the east to Iceland, Greenland and, for a while, Newfoundland in the west. But their apparently inexorably spread was halted by worsening weather. Life on Iceland had initially been prosperous for the Vikings, who were the first people to colonise the island on the edge of the Arctic Circle. But the little ice age brought a serious decline and the island was often cut off by ice.

However, the worst tragedy befell one of the farthest-flung Viking settlements, on Greenland. The land had never been exactly green. Its name was coined by Leif

Hunters in the snow: as Europe froze during the little ice age, Brueghel painted many such snow scenes.

A warm, wet summer brought potato blight to Ireland in the 1840s: millions died in the famine that followed.

Erikson, one of the pioneering kings of the Viking world, to attract settlers to join him. He was a persuasive estate agent and many people followed. But the winters began to close in, the seas froze and icebergs made the trip from Scandinavia increasingly dangerous. After 100 years or so, there was a silent thaw before the little ice age closed in again. 'After somewhere around AD 1400,' says Lamb, 'no ships really established any form of communication with the white population of Greenland.'

They were cut off and apparently unable to adapt their lives to a hostile land. Graves excavated by archaeologists at Herjolfsnes, once the main commercial centre on the southern tip of Greenland, reveal that within a few generations the average height of the Greenland Vikings fell from 5 ft 10 in to 5 ft 2 in. 'It was a bitter time,' says Lamb. 'The declining population must have lived through some awful years.' Many malnourished bodies, buried in soft soil, became permanently frozen and covered by glaciers. The bodies have been released from that icy grip only in recent decades, their clothing fully preserved. The women's bodies were so deformed that they would have been incapable of bearing children.

The story may offer a warning to our own civilisation. The Vikings appear to have succumbed to their fate almost wilfully, failing to adapt to changing climate. As the weather cooled, the Eskimos of northern Greenland moved south, probably following the seals that they hunted. The Europeans should have copied them, taking up fishing and trapping. But instead they stuck with their hens and sheep and built ever bigger churches in the hope that God would save them. He did not. After 400 years the Viking colony in Greenland died out.

The onset of the little ice age shows up in the USA as well. Scientists have investigated how tree rings there vary according to climate, with thick rings forming round the tree's trunk during wet years and thin rings during years of drought. They have plotted these rings in the wooden buildings, grain stores and other structures built by American Indians. The result is a detailed year-by-year analysis of when Indians colonised the drier parts of the American West.

Dennie O'Bowden, from the Tree Ring Laboratory at the University of Arizona in Tucson, says 'In the tree rings of archaeological remains, we see the Indians of the southwest forming more complex civilisations starting round AD 900–1000,' before the advent of the little ice age. 'But somewhere around 1150 we see the disintegration of the cultures.' The rings reveal that the land was becoming drier at that time, and the rest of the archaeological remains show that farming was no longer possible on the plains of the American West. The farmers moved to new regions of New Mexico and Arizona, where Indian farmers, such as the Hopi, live to this day. There was a long period of severe drought in the second half of the thirteenth century in the west of the USA, as well as in Europe.

Meanwhile the old plains were taken over by other groups of Indians who lived by hunting animals and gathering wild plants. They could cope with the new arid environment of the region. 'It looks like the loss of rainfall caused the more complex

Indian communities with cities, totally dependent on agricultural supplies and storage, to collapse,' says O'Bowden.

Scotland the cold

Scottish nationalists must rue the little ice age, for without it there might have been no union with England. That, at any rate, is Lamb's view. The first couple of centuries of the little ice age had no marked effect on Scotland. Indeed, the thirteenth century is sometimes called the golden age of Scotland. But the fourteenth and fifteenth centuries brought chill winds blowing across the highlands and the country fell into ferment. Says Lamb: 'The highland troubles that occupy so much of Sir Walter Scott's writings are one of the most serious parts of Scottish history, with the highland raids into the lowlands. I think they were really a story of the deteriorating climate as much as anything. In the more genial years of the thirteenth century, farms and habitations had been established far up the glens in positions that were not really sustainable in the years that followed. When some of the worst phases of the climate approached in the 1420s and 1430s, the whole central highlands were in a state of great unrest. I think they just hadn't enough to eat.'

During the 1430s, when the great highland estate ruled by the Earls of Mar broke down, the highlanders used bark to make their bread. 'The wretches had to eat and a natural recourse was to raid the more prosperous farmers on the lowlands. The whole society in consequence became very insecure and in 1437 the king was murdered on the fringes of the highlands.' There was famine elsewhere in Europe as the cold bit hard. Wolves raided villages in England, apparently for the last time.

The little ice age continued, however, and throughout Britain reached its coldest phase in the final years of the seventeenth century. 'Those were the years in which the sea ice advanced furthest south,' says Lamb. In 1695, ice cut off Iceland totally from the outside world for most of the year. The ice extended as far south as the Shetland Islands. Fisheries failed totally there as well as across the Norwegian Sea.

London may have enjoyed its frost fairs, but some estimates put the loss of life in those grim years at up to half of the populations of Norway and Sweden and a third of that of Denmark. Further south the glaciers of the Alps spread down their valleys and the hill farms of England were abandoned. In the highland parishes of Scotland the grain harvest failed for seven years between 1693 and 1700. The hungry gathered harvests of nettles to eat and the number of people who died of starvation and disease in Scotland exceeded the toll during the Black Death. The clans fought once more and the king lost control of his country. In the Scottish parliament, the grain barons of the lowlands were arraigned for ignoring the plight of the highlanders.

The consequences of this protracted crisis remain with us to this day. 'The final outcome,' Lamb says, 'was the union of the parliaments of Scotland and England 1707. I don't know that Scotland had very much alternative. There had been harvest failures from the late 1500s onwards in the highlands and the islands of the west.'

The climatic events of the seventeenth century also triggered the beginning of a long sad chapter in the history of Ireland, because as a result King James set up the first Protestant settlements in Northern Ireland. James responded to repeated threats of famine in Scotland 'by planting some of his population who were in difficulties in the west of Scotland into Ulster', says Lamb.

Irish skies

One way or another, climate has played a fundamental role in the history of Ireland. The country prospered during the little ice age while others froze. So it was well able to receive settlers sent there from Scotland by King James. But 200 years later climate caused the appalling famine that struck the country. Ireland was one of the first places in Europe to adopt the potato in the seventeenth century. The import from South America yielded four times as much carbohydrate per acre as wheat. It was also resilient to climatic stress and much more reliable than the then ubiquitous rye, which was often afflicted by ergot blight, a fungal poison that caused a disease of the central nervous system called St Anthony's Fire.

The potato was an important reason for Ireland's prosperity. 'It was regarded as a godsend by the Irish,' says Mick Kelly, one of Lamb's colleagues at the Climatic Research Unit. 'It enabled the population of Ireland to increase at a rate greater than its European neighbours during the seventeenth and eighteenth centuries. However, by the 1840s, the Irish population was almost totally reliant on the potato as its food supply, and that proved quite catastrophic.'

Potato blight arrived in Europe from the Americas in 1845 and spread rapidly from Flanders right across western Europe, reaching Ireland in September. The weather, with temperature high and rainfall abundant, was the key to the spread, but Ireland's peculiar dependence on the potato left it uniquely vulnerable, since there was no other source of food. The poor grew only potatoes and the English landlords continued to export wheat from their estates. Over a million people died in Ireland during the six years of the blight, from starvation or disease brought on by hunger.

Through the 1840s and 1850s, the population of Ireland was decimated, first by famine (which lasted from 1845 to 1849) and then by migration. In fact, the population diminished from 8.5 million to around 3 million during the 1850s. It never recovered. Today, the total population of the island is only 4.5 million.

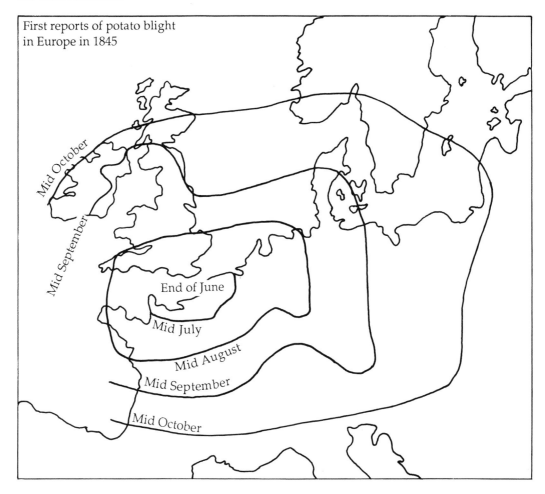

First reports of potato blight
in Europe in 1845

Mid October

Mid September

End of June

Mid July

Mid August

Mid September

Mid October

Sun spots

What caused the little ice age? The answer, say some researchers, is sunspots. Astronomers have seen spots on the surface of the sun for the past 300 years, though accurate measurement and counting is much more recent. Sunspots indicate intense solar activity, which is blasting radiation into outer space. They wax and wane on a cycle roughly 11 years long.

During 1989 the sun was passing through a period of intense activity with increased interference to radio and TV communications and the dramatic appearance of 'northern lights', which were seen right across England one night in late March. Modern satellites have confirmed a long-held suspicion that sunspots also indicate that more solar heat reaches the Earth. While the extra heat is only a fraction of 1 per cent of the total output of the sun, it is sufficient to alter slightly the circulation of the winds and ocean currents, and to have an impact on weather shows that up in tree rings, for instance.

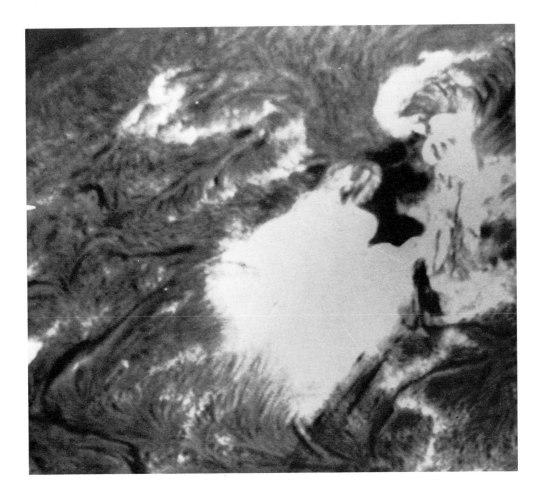

Solar flares, such as these photographed in March 1989, may influence our weather, but Jack Eddy of the National Center for Atmospheric Research at Boulder, Colorado, says that the sun has been kind to us.

Victorian meteorologists paid great attention to sunspots in the hope of using them to predict the catastrophic failures of the Indian monsoon. Since then, people have tried to show that the sunspot cycle is responsible for everything from the stock exchange index to the hemline of skirts.

Jack Eddy from the USA's National Center for Atmospheric Research in Boulder, Colorado, has attempted to sort truth from fiction. He finds it hard. 'There's a very interesting connection between the sunspot cycle and the quality of Burgundy wine. It allows people like me, who don't know much about wines but know where we are in the sunspot cycle, to order wine intelligently.' On the other hand, he muses, such connections may be 'more a reflection on ourselves than on the sun. We yearn for regularity. We would like to have something in nature that's predictable so that we can use it to predict the future.'

Eddy believes that the sun's effect on the day-to-day weather is very small. 'But there does seem to be a statistically strong link between sunspots and American droughts. Researchers into tree rings discovered a decade ago evidence that every two sun-spot cycles (that is, every 22 years) there tends to be a drought in the western part of the USA.' Even more important may be longer-term trends in the strength of the peaks in sunspot activity. Eddy singles out the whole of the little ice age as a time of very low solar activity. The sunspot cycle more or less disappeared, with sunspots almost non-existent on the surface of the sun for several centuries. The result was a cooler planet and major changes in climatic systems. For instance, during the 1690s, the Gulf Stream faltered drastically.

'The present hundred years during which we have studied the sun most intently have been a time of relative calm and benign behaviour by the star', says Eddy. Besides the steady rhythm of the sunspot cycle, nothing untoward has occurred. The only certainty, however, is that this will not last for ever. So, could we be approaching another little ice age? Tom Wigley thinks we could, at any rate within the next 500 years.

Carbon dating

As so often, evidence for the future comes from analysis of the past. One method is analysis of variations in the amount of a particular radioactive isotope, known as carbon-14, in the rings of trees. Measuring carbon-14 is widely known as a method of dating organic material. Any piece of living flesh or plant material contains a number of isotopes of carbon. Once a tree dies, the radioactive carbon-14 in it decays, turning gradually into other isotopes. Since the half-life of carbon-14 is known, the theory is that its age at death can be calculated.

In practice, things are not quite so simple because the amount of carbon-14 in the atmosphere (and hence in the living organism) is not constant. There is a carbon-14 'wiggle'. So carbon-14 dating is not very accurate. Luckily, scientists have another method of checking dates, using tree rings, which provide an absolutely unambiguous record of the date of a piece of wood. By using this cross-check, they can plot the wiggles. The result is interesting.

'If we look back at the history of these carbon-14 wiggles we find that there may be 15 or 20 of them in the last 8000 years,' said Wigley. At a conference in early 1989 it was suggested that the wiggles may be regular, with a 200-year cycle that coincides tantalisingly with little ice ages. Wigley agrees that the wiggles coincide with advances and retreats of alpine glaciers and with changes in the output of the sun. The records of carbon-14 wiggles show that, in the years since the end of the last ice age, there have been a long series of little ice ages, caused by changes in the output of the sun. The effect of each has been about a quarter of that predicted for the next few decades from the greenhouse effect, so a new little ice age won't halt a greenhouse warming, but it would help moderate it a little.

For Eddy the sun remains a chaotic enigma. 'What we'd like to know is how the overall activity of the sun will change over the next 10 years—say, how it is going to support or take from the greenhouse effect. But the sun is not that regular. The 11-year cycle comes and goes but that cycle is sometimes swollen and sometimes drops in ways that are very hard to predict. I think I can make one prediction—that the sun is never going to hurt us very badly. It's a very benign star. It varies, but we can count on it to rise and set every day and, I think, to provide most of our needs. In the very long picture, our sun will do what the others stars in the sky do. In many billions of years into the future, it will gradually expand, grow redder and in the process become so bright that it will end life on Earth. That time is so far away, however, that only poets need think about it.'

CHAPTER 5

Under the volcano

Besides the sun and human activity, there are a number of natural events on Earth that can influence climate over the short term and upset the weather. One is volcanoes. When a large volcano erupts it can put into the upper atmosphere huge amounts of very fine dust that block the sunlight and cool the surface of the planet. Tiny sulphate particles, emitted in large amounts from volcanic eruptions, are the most effective barrier, reflecting sunlight of a certain wavelength back into space.

Not all volcanoes change our climate, however. The eruption of Mount St Helens in the USA in 1980, for instance, had little effect on the upper atmosphere because it exploded sideways rather than vertically. Its dust swiftly fell to Earth. The largest recent volcanic explosion was El Chichon in Mexico in 1982. It brought rather less publicity than Mount St Helens, but threw much more dust into the upper atmosphere. El Chichon 'took so much dust that it lasted for years in the strato-sphere,' says Alan Robock, an American meteorologist from the University of Maryland. Graphs of worldwide temperatures show a dip in a strong warming trend of several tenths of a degree in 1984, which researchers attribute to the impact of dust from El Chichon.

Robock believes that volcanoes can cool the planet for several years. The initial cooling of the air caused by the dust enables more ice to form in the oceans. The ice reflects the sun's heat and cools the planet further. After the dust clears, the oceans take some time to melt that ice. This timelag is accentuated because volcanic dust disappears last of all from the air over the poles. So, as Hubert Lamb points out, 'sea ice might get a boost for quite some years from a great eruption.' Robock estimates that it could take a decade for temperatures to return to normal after a large eruption. But his case is difficult to reconcile with the sharp warming through-out the 1980s, which saw a record world temperature set both before and after the eruption of El Chichon.

Most researchers think that volcanoes have only a relatively short-lived effect on climate. But Robock claims that a fall in the frequency of large eruptions could be responsible for an increase in average temperatures seen over the past century. This increase is often attributed to the early stages of a greenhouse warming, but Robock points out that at the end of the nineteenth century there were several major volcanic eruptions which would have kept temperatures artificially low. The biggest of these was the explosion of the volcanic island of Krakatoa in the East

Indies in 1883. The sound of the explosion was heard 4500 kilometres away in Australia and its dust formed a veil round the Earth that produced brilliant sunsets for several years.

In the 1930s and 1940s there were 'virtually no volcanoes' erupting, says Robock – and the world was warmer. 'That was the time,' he says, 'when people first said it was the greenhouse effect at work. But from then on temperatures were relatively constant for about 40 years 'and that was a period when we started having volcanic eruptions again.'

Perhaps the most traumatic volcanic eruption of recent centuries, beating even the destruction of Krakatoa, was the eruption of Tambora, again in the East Indies, in April 1815. The eruption is reckoned to have been the largest anywhere in the world since 1500 and it put into the atmosphere around 80 cubic kilometres of debris. That was followed in 1816 by the 'year without a summer'. The weather was very cold, gloomy and rainy throughout Europe. It ruined harvests, and prices on the London Grain Exchange reached a record high.

It is arguable that Tambora set off huge social changes in North America. In 1816 there was snow every month during the summer in New England. 'Farmers would plant crops, they would die, they'd plant them again and it ruined the harvest then, too. That was the beginning of a lot of migration out to the Midwest of the USA because people couldn't survive in the East,' says Robock. And recent analysis of Chinese documents shows cold, stormy weather and bad harvests in both 1816 and 1817. On Hainan Island in the tropical South China Sea, frost destroyed crops, grass disappeared and more than half of the trees died. In nearby Taiwan, inch-thick ice formed on the ground. Evidence of such drastic effects from three continents has led researchers to agree with Robock that the effect of Tambora 'seems to have been global'.

Perhaps the best known story from the 'year without a summer' concerns the poet Lord Byron who was staying on the shores of Lake Geneva in Switzerland with his friends the Shelleys. The cold forced the party to remain indoors, where they wrote. Mary Shelley was so depressed that she wrote *Frankenstein*, and Byron composed a poem called 'Darkness', which, says Robock, 'sounds like the beginning of a nuclear winter'.

> The bright sun was extinguish'd, and the stars
> Did wander darkling in the eternal space,
> Rayless, and pathless, and the icy earth
> Swung blind and blackening in the moonless air;
> Morn came and went—and came, and brought no day,
> And men forgot their passions in the dread
> Of this their desolation. . . .

On the equator

Another source of natural short-term fluctuations in the world's climate is a reversal of wind and ocean currents that occurs every few years in the Pacific Ocean. It is called 'El Niño', Spanish for 'the boy' (meaning the Christ child). It got its name because an ocean current that heralds its onset often occurs off Peru around Christmas time. 'El Niño' influences climate around the world, causing drought in Australia, India and parts of Africa and torrential rains in the deserts of South America.

David Anderson of the Hooke Institute at Oxford University writes computer models of ocean currents. 'In 1982 and 1983 there was the largest 'El Niño' event that we have ever experienced,' he says. Storm clouds that normally form over the western Pacific, near Indonesia 'slowly began to migrate ... all the way to the eastern Pacific. It was associated with very large changes in climate. In Australia they had one of the worst droughts in 200 years, with huge bush fires, while in the east huge floods occurred all over Ecuador and in parts of Peru.' The damage to Australia probably exceeded £1 billion and may have been similar in South America, says Anderson. The Peruvian fishing industry was almost wiped out as warm water (the 'El Niño' current itself) blocked out the nutrient-rich polar waters that usually flow up the coast of South America. The wildlife of the Galapagos Islands, which inspired Charles Darwin to develop his theories about the origin of species, almost died out. Many people died too, as the bush fires in Australia reached the suburbs of Melbourne, and forest fires raged across Borneo for three months. Around 100 000 people lost their homes during the floods in South America.

'El Niños' normally happen every 3–5 years. Their starting point is the tropical western Pacific Ocean where, at around 27°C, ocean temperatures are the hottest anywhere and much warmer than in the eastern Pacific. The tropical rain clouds of the western Pacific, fuelled by the hot ocean waters, make islands such as Borneo and New Guinea some of the wettest places in the world.

The region of the western Pacific is one of three places on the Earth's surface that act in effect as radiators for the planet. Heat from the sun is the force that drives the world's climate and which maintains temperatures. The sun's heat is absorbed mainly at the equator and then transported by the atmosphere and oceans towards the poles. The first stage of this process is the formation of giant storm clouds, vast packets of the sun's energy. This happens at three areas along the equator: the western Pacific and the Amazon and Congo rainforest regions. The western Pacific heat source is unique because it is not tied to a spot of land. It can move and, periodically, it does. The result is 'El Niño'.

'El Niño' events occur when the warm water of the western Pacific surges eastwards, along with accompanying storm clouds. This seems to happen once the western Pacific reaches some critical temperature, after which the heat has to 'break out' by moving east. Over the following months the warm waters surge east for up to 10 000 miles until they hit the far shore of the Pacific, around Peru and Ecuador, causing torrential rains in areas that are normally deserts. The warm waters then bounce back and mix with the cooler waters coming in behind. 'El Niño', at that point, is over. But the return trip, as cold water washes westwards across the oceans causes almost as much havoc, as events during 1988 and 1989 proved.

This stage of the 'El Niño' cycle now has its own name, 'La Niña', adopted because anti-'El Niño', meaning literally anti-Christ, was considered blasphemous. Following an 'El Niño' event in 1987, a strong 'La Niña' took place during the following two years, cooling much of the Pacific Ocean and bringing intense storms to many parts of eastern Asia and Australia, where 20 people were killed and thousands of animals drowned. During late 1988 there were floods as record rains hit Bangladesh and Sudan, two places where drought often accompanies the main phase of 'El Niños'. Many climatologists blamed 'La Niña' for the drought that hit the Midwestern states of the USA in 1988. One consequence of the poor harvest was that the grain shortage was to cut the world's food reserves by half.

What exactly causes the build-up of heat in the western Pacific, and why it should suddenly break out, remains unclear. But the course of 'El Niño' and 'La Niña' can now be predicted several months ahead and data about ocean temperatures have been used to predict rainfall in the drought-prone regions of Ethiopia and Sudan.

Oceanographers are now engaged in a major international science project called TOGA (for Tropical Ocean/Global Atmosphere) to probe the mechanisms behind these events. They believe that both 'El Niño' and 'La Niña' are part of a continuous oscillation of the tropical Pacific, with each accumulation of heat in the west of the ocean an inevitable consequence of the last.

Whatever its precise cause, 'El Niño' has been recognised in the 1980s as a major perturbation of the planet's climatic systems. Among other things, it shifts so much water across the Pacific Ocean that it seems to affect the rotation of the earth, adding and taking away fractions of seconds from the day.

'El Niños' may be closely related to the Asian monsoon. Monsoons are essentially giant sea breezes. In summer the land heats up and hot air rises, creating a zone of low air pressure into which winds rush from over the oceans. The monsoon winds of Asia become entangled with those of the western Pacific. In this way, says Anderson, an 'El Niño' event may drag the western Pacific wind systems across the ocean away from Asia. Then, the Indian monsoon fails. 'It is quite frequently the case,' he says, 'that there will be drought over large parts of India following a major 'El Niño' event.' There also seems to be a link between 'El Niño' and drought in Africa. Certainly, the great drought of 1983 coincided eerily with the major 'El Niño' recorded on the other side of the planet.

One of the more important questions about our planet's future as human activities start to change our weather is how apparently hair-trigger switches in our natural climate, such as 'El Niño', will respond. There is great potential for sudden catastrophic events, quite different from the gradual changes predicted by many computer models.

On a knife edge

One man who is more insistent than most that the systems that rule our climate are ever vulnerable to sudden shifts is Wally Broecker from the Lamonts-Doherty Geographical Observatory at Columbia University. He warns that the world could be in for some sudden and unpleasant shocks, perhaps within the next ten years or so, as we enter the greenhouse age. For Broecker the key era of the past that offers lessons for the future is the end of the most recent ice age. It was a time when climate changed almost as rapidly as today. Yet the processes were entirely natural.

'The ice age had built up and built up for about 100 000 years and then all of a sudden, 14 000 years ago, bingo! It went away,' says Broecker. 'In about a thousand years, the poles warmed up and the snowlines on the mountains receded to where they are today. What could have caused this very pronounced change in such a short time?'

Ice melts too slowly to explain the suddenness of events, he says. And he is sceptical of the theory that plankton in the oceans are capable of causing such changes. He has a different explanation. He thinks it was caused by the circulation of the oceans which can change extremely fast. At the end of the ice age, says Broecker, there was a rapid 'reorganisation of the oceanic system' that switched the world's climate into a new order.

The great circulation systems in the oceans drag surface waters down to the depths over very long cycles, possibly hundreds of years. The reason for this is salt redistribution, made necessary because the winds evaporate water from the oceans and leave behind salt. In normal times, winds evaporate huge amounts of water from the warm North Atlantic and dump it as rain thousands of kilometres away in the cooler northern Pacific Ocean. So the Atlantic becomes saltier while the Pacific becomes fresher. A deep ocean current, which Broecker likens to a conveyor belt, redresses the salt balance by transporting salty water along the bottom of the oceans from the Atlantic to the Pacific. During ice ages, this conveyor belt shuts down when the growth of ice sheets stops evaporation from the North Atlantic. At the end of each ice age, the current returns. These reorganisations, which may happen in less than a century are, says Broecker, 'profound and they change a lot of things on the surface of the Earth.'

One thing they change is the climate of Europe. The mild weather of modern western Europe is almost entirely dependent on the oceans. Francis Bretherton, a British climatologist who emigrated to the USA and works at the University of Wisconsin, says: 'When I first moved to the USA, the cold winters took some getting used to.' This he found odd, since he had actually moved south. He looked at the map and discovered that Europe was the oddity. London is the same distance from the north pole as the southern tip of Hudson Bay in Canada, which is icebound for nine months of the year. 'The climate of northwestern Europe is really rather special,' he says. 'It is determined to a large extent by the Gulf Stream, a warm ocean current that crosses the North Atlantic and moves northwards past Britain into the Norwegian Sea. If the Gulf Stream was to change, the climate of the British Isles would change substantially with it.'

And the Gulf Stream does change, says Bretherton. 'When we look at the geological record, we find that the Gulf Stream did not always go the way it goes now.' During ice ages, rather than bringing warm waters north to bathe the shores of Britain and Scandinavia, 'it went straight across the Atlantic Ocean to Gibraltar.'

Bretherton has a warning for his former homeland. 'We must expect that over the next 50–100 years as the temperature warms up, those currents may well change too, with consequences that are really very difficult to foresee but could be quite important for Europe.' Broecker picks up the theme. The Gulf Stream is an essential link in his global conveyor belt. Shut down the conveyor, as happened in the last ice age, and the Gulf Stream weakens or fails and Europe's winters become 10°C colder.

Human activity might, says Broecker, cause the system to switch again. If the greenhouse effect changes patterns of rainfall and evaporation—perhaps by stopping the formation of ice in the far North Atlantic—then the conveyor belt could once again fail. 'We're playing,' he says, 'with a system that is not resilient. It's very sensitive and it can do some very strange things.'

Broecker believes that the world must start preparing for the possibility of some sudden, totally unexpected change in climate. 'The important thing,' he says, 'is to start thinking carefully about what to do if the system does this. How would the world react to it? How do we prevent panic? It would be like a drought starting and never coming to an end. We're thinking of this happening maybe between the years 2040 and 2100. That's the time when there are going to be 10 billion people on the planet. We're going to be pushing very hard to feed those people, to keep them happy and to keep them from shooting nuclear weapons at each other.' This is the kind of talk that makes the conventional ideas about the greenhouse effect sound cosy by comparison.

El Chicon, a Mexican volcano, erupted in 1982, filling the upper atmosphere with dust, cooling the planet in 1984.

'El Niño', a reversal of winds and ocean currents across the Pacific, helped bring drought and famine to Ethiopia in 1983. Here, relatives prepare an emaciated body for burial. . . .

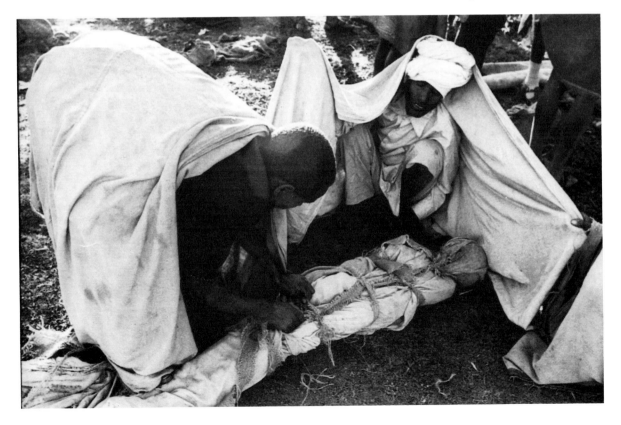

... In 1988, Pacific winds and currents changed again, bringing floods to Bangladesh.

Snow blanketed Britain during record-breaking cold winters in 1947 and 1963.

CHAPTER 6

Taking the planet's temperature

The past decade has been the warmest on record in most of the world. Temperatures have been up to 1°C warmer on average round the globe than a century ago, though Britain has yet to see much evidence of this. Most of the hottest individual years on record have also been in the 1980s, headed by 1988, just ahead of 1987 and 1983. Climatologists have a strong hunch that this warming of the planet is due to the greenhouse effect. But they say that it could be a decade or more before they can be absolutely certain. Such are the difficulties that they have both in making accurate comparisons with past temperatures and in separating out the natural variability of climate from any greenhouse warming.

There are many sources of climatic variability that will show up even when looking at average temperatures for the whole globe. During and for a few months after a strong 'El Niño' event, the world is warmer. This is largely a knock-on effect of the heating of the tropical Pacific Ocean as the warm waters of the western ocean spread to cover the width of the ocean and prevent colder water from reaching the surface. So the 'El Niño' of 1982–83 was accompanied by a record warm year. The 'El Niño' of 1987, though less intense, brought new temperature records in 1987 and 1988. Conversely, during 'La Niñas' the world tends to cool. That trend was clear in 1984 (though El Chichon may have had a hand) and in data collected during the second half of 1988. It was expected to last through 1989, leading to a cooling of the planet, for a while at any rate.

Some researchers believe that 'El Niños' may have a ratchet effect in raising temperatures; but equally 'La Niñas' may bring the thermometers of the world back down again. In 1990 and 1991 researchers will be looking hard for evidence about whether the planet becomes cooler following the strong 'La Niña' of the late 1980s. If it does, then there could be some red faces and radical rethinks among the greenhouse fraternity.

Tom Wigley does not underestimate the problems of charting changes in the world's climate. One vital area for investigation is why the warming of the past century faltered and almost went into reverse between 1940 and 1975. 'That's really interesting because if the greenhouse effect was the only factor operating, we would have expected a substantial warming over that period,' he says.

Another unanswered question is why global average temperatures may differ by several tenths of a degree from year to year. 'This doesn't sound like very much,'

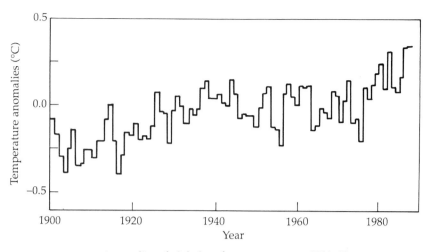

Anomalies of global surface temperature, 1901–88.

says Lamb, 'but it does mean a tremendous change in the amount of heat absorbed by the lower parts of the atmosphere. Those year-to-year variations are not properly explained.' It is these individual years of great warmth or cold that people remember, rather than slow trends. Without being told, few people would know that there was a long period of global warming during the first four decades of this century. But many will remember that at the close of that warming period there was a series of long hot summers, during which the Battle of Britain was fought out in clear blue skies in 1940. Then, as warming faltered, came the cold winters (in Britain and Europe) of 1947 and 1963, when the whole of Britain was covered in a thick blanket of snow for the first time since the end of the little ice age, and the sea at Southend froze.

The 1960s and early 1970s were so cold that there was serious talk among scientists and in lengthy newspaper articles that the world was suddenly sliding towards a new ice age. Then, when Britain had its record hot and dry summer of 1976, global warming resumed. Reservoirs emptied, forcing Britain to contemplate its vulnerability even to a small change in climate. Through most of the 1980s, however, there was nothing that the British could identify to show that the world in general was undergoing a substantial warming. Nothing, that is, until the exceptionally warm winter of 1988–89.

There are almost as many examples of weather that bucks the trend as cases that illustrate it. Tom Wigley of the Climatic Research Unit is as interested in the oddities of climatic change as in the broad trends. Ultimately, it could be in these inconsistencies that scientists find the clues to a whole range of influences on our climate. 'For example,' he says, 'in global mean terms there was a warm period around the late 1930s and early 1940s. But if you look at Europe during the early 1940s there were some warm summers but there were some terribly cold winters and those winters are in striking contrast to the global mean. In the 1970s, there

45

was the drought and very hot summers in Europe in 1975 and 1976. The summer of 1976 in Europe was one of the hottest summers on record. Yet we know that 1976 was a very cold year globally.'

Another example is the winter of 1962–63. It was one of the most severe winters of the past 300 years in Europe. 'Now, globally, 1962–63 wasn't terribly cold; but if I move forward one year, 1964 was a very cold year,' says Wigley. 'Without knowing the cause, incautious researchers might link the cold European winter of 1963 with the cold global temperatures of 1964. But most of the reason for 1964 being cool was the eruption of a volcano called Agung on the Indonesian island of Bali.' Since Europe's cold winter preceded that eruption, 'there is no relation between those two.'

Lamb has looked at another index of natural variability. It is often pointed out, as an unambiguous sign of global warming, that glaciers round the world—from the Alps to Kenya—have been in retreat for the past century. This is true as far as it goes. The Rhône glacier in the Alps is a well-documented example. Over the past 80 years, it has retreated by almost half a mile up its valley, exposing rock scoured smooth by the force of a thousand feet of ice. Yet, Lamb says, 'over half of the glaciers of Europe have been advancing since the early 1960s. There was quite a turn-round at that time. And the latest report I have seen is that in Sweden the ice has advanced a bit in the 1980s. At least this part of the world is misbehaving as regards global warming.' The world may be warming, but Europe has been getting colder.

Heat islands and cold decks

The business of assessing trends in temperatures is critically dependent on the quality of data from past decades and how comparable they are with current measurements. The biggest problem in measuring temperatures round the globe is that more than two-thirds of the planet is covered by oceans. 'Fortunately,' Wigley says, 'because ships are so dependent on weather forecasts, sailors have been collecting meteorological information for 150 years or so.' They have measured the temperature of the oceans by lowering buckets into the waves, pulling them back on to the deck and putting a thermometer in. The total data bank now includes some 400 million measurements taken over the past century.

Unfortunately, instruments and techniques have changed during that time. This may have improved the accuracy of the measurements, but it has made comparisons with past decades difficult. In the mid-nineteenth century sailors took water samples with wooden buckets. Until around 1940, they used canvas buckets. Since then they have measured the temperature of water taken into the boat to cool the engines of the ship. These differences could all produce a small but systematic change in temperatures recorded at sea. Researchers have had to work out whether wooden buckets might heat up water more or less than canvas ones,

During the 1980s, many of the world's glaciers such as the Columbia Glacier in Alaska have retreated as the climate warms.

Even in the desert, cities such as Phoenix, Arizona, increase the heat.

how long the buckets sat on the deck before measurements were taken, and whether this would be long enough to alter the temperature of the water. 'What we have to do is factor out the non-climatic effects so that we're left with a pure climatic signal. That is quite a difficult and time-consuming task but we believe that we've done it fairly precisely,' says Wigley.

There are also problems about comparing thermometer measurements made on land. One important source of interference is the urban heat island effect. 'If someone has a meteorological station located in a city, even if there is no climatic change, the temperatures for that particular site would almost certainly have increased during the twentieth century. This is because of the growth of the urbanised area and because people now use more energy and inject more waste heat into the environment,' says Wigley.

Cities are normally much warmer than the surrounding countryside, especially in the early morning in winter. Recent studies have shown that temperatures in the early morning today are 10° higher in some parts of the fast-growing desert city of Phoenix in Arizona than they were 20 years ago. Concrete and asphalt hold the sun's heat through the night far better than the surrounding desert sands. Curiously, another study, at the equally fast-growing community of Palm Springs in California, discovered no such warming. It turned out that a strong 'golf course effect' was keeping the desert town cool. Apparently, the town contains many golf courses where so much water is poured on to the grass to keep the greens green that a lot of heat energy is expended in evaporating this water, thus keeping down local temperatures.

Researchers have attempted to filter out the urban heat-island effect from their data by looking for changes in the difference between urban and rural temperatures. They reduce urban temperatures in their records to compensate.

California

In this statistical quagmire, there is some solace in analysing changes in climate by looking at tree rings. Malcolm Hughes of the Tree Ring Laboratory at the University of Wisconsin in the USA has in his laboratory the stump of a sequoia or redwood tree felled in central California early in this century. It carries a continuous 3000-year record of its environment from 995 BC to AD 1914. During dry years, the tree grew little, leaving a ring about a millimetre across; during wetter years it grew faster, leaving a broad ring. Its outer rings reveal a period of wet weather in California starting in 1612, for instance.

Other trees reveal for this century 'a handful of really quite severe droughts in California and in a big region of the coastal American West in 1924 and 1959–61 and 1977, in particular,' says Hughes. They will be recording another three-year drought in the final years of the 1980s. Tree rings allow researchers to 'take a particular summer, say 1066, and see what happened in California, in North Carolina, in northern Sweden, maybe even in the Forest of Dean, and put together a picture of how hot and dry, or cool and wet, it was in many different parts of the world. Taken together, they provide the footprint of that year's climate.'

One discovery from this approach is that drought years in California often coincide with miserable, wet and cold years in Britain. 'We're trying to take those kind of patterns to see if there's a real connection in the weather,' says Hughes. 'If there is, that's going to tell us about the behaviour of the whole system.' It might, for instance, confirm tantalising hints that there may be a connection between 'El Niño' and the weather of Europe. The climate of California is certainly partly linked to 'El Niño' events. The state's normally benign weather was interrupted by giant storms and floods triggered by 'El Niño' in 1983, disrupting Queen Elizabeth II's visit to the state.

There will be lessons in this for plotting future changes in climate. It may be that the patterns repeat themselves. If the deserts of the American southwest grow in the greenhouse world, as some models predict, then perhaps Europe will become cool and wet. Some would say that is precisely what happened in the 1980s. Or again, the patterns may change in the future, suggesting a profound upheaval of the climatic systems.

Hughes's tree-ring data already reveal fascinating glimpses of recent climatic changes, which may or may not be connected to the early stages of greenhouse warming. 'Since 1850,' he says, 'across Alaska and the northern part of the Soviet Union, we see increases in tree growth that appear to be related to increases in temperature in those places. We see a similar thing in the Alps, in the Rockies, in high mountain places where they have a cool moist summer.' Down in the dry regions, for example in the Central Valley of California, there have been a series of four or five major droughts, not seen on such a scale, according to the tree-ring record, since about AD 800.

'We've seen right round the world the tendency for rainfall to decline in the past couple of decades in the tropical desert regions, such as the Sahel in Africa. At the same time, there has been an increase in rainfall in temperate latitudes such as western Europe and northern Canada and, in the southern hemisphere, New Zealand.' In general, says Hughes, where it has got warmer, it has also become drier. 'We don't know if that will hold.'

What does this most recent trend mean? Mick Kelly at the Climatic Research Unit is alarmed at the coincidence of drying subtropics and dampening temperate zones. 'It's almost as though the north is stealing the Third World's water,' he says. 'These trends began about the time that the world first warmed significantly in the 1930s and 1940s. The drought in Africa is the most pronounced manifestation of the trend, but it has affected other areas as well. And I think we have to raise the question: is the drought in Africa the first tangible manifestation, the first substantial impact of global warming? We don't know for sure; there are many possible causes

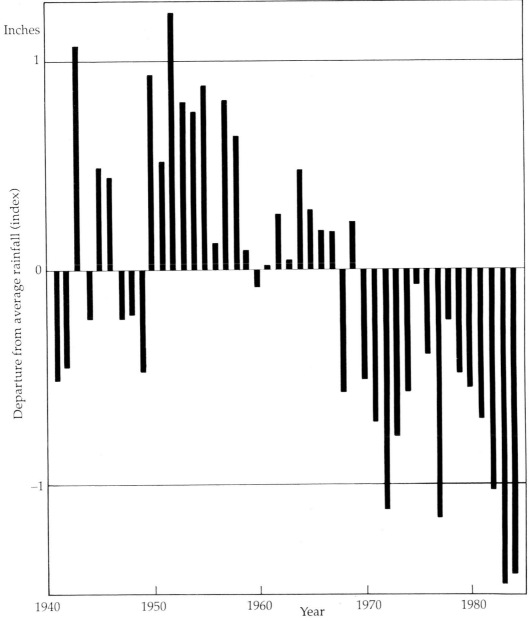

How rainfall has diminished in the Sahel.

of that drought, but it would be a sad comment on our ability as scientists if, in concentrating on global temperature as an indicator of the greenhouse effect, we actually missed out on the first tragic impact of global warming.'

PART TWO

A Change in the Weather

CHAPTER 1

Weather eyes open

On 22nd June 1941, Hitler launched his invasion of the Soviet Union. His spring had been taken up with the Balkan campaign and it was perhaps a little late in the year to march on Moscow. But Franz Baur, a senior meteorologist in the Wehrmacht and a specialist in long-range forecasting, thought not. The autumn, he had predicted, would be mild and dry. The invading army swept through Russia. By October it was within 150 kilometres of Moscow. Then the bad weather came. First, rain bogged down the troops, then snow froze them. It was so cold that the firing pins of the German weapons snapped and the greatest army in the world had to do battle with the Red Army using trenching tools and bayonets. Baur was so nonplussed that, on hearing over the telephone from the front how cold it was, he replied: 'The observations must be wrong.'

Arguably, this meteorological mistake cost Hitler the war. If the rains had held off, Hitler might have reached Moscow. Ironically, another team of meteorologists working for the Luftwaffe, analysing the upper atmosphere rather than using Baur's surface charts, was predicting a severe Russian winter.

World history can be changed by the weather. The French Revolution may have been triggered by record bread prices following a bad summer. On the day before the revolutionaries stormed the Bastille in July 1789, wheat prices reached a new high in Paris, according to the historian Le Roy Ladurie. A mild winter saved Amsterdam from French conquest in 1673. Fortunes too may depend on the weather. The financier who can predict frosts in Brazil can retire on the proceeds of a single kill in the coffee futures market. Norman Lynagh works for the Noble Denton Weather Service in London, providing specialist weather forecasts for everyone from supermarkets to the offshore oil industry. One of his clients is a commodity broker with an interest in potatoes. 'I don't think they actually see potatoes themselves,' says Lynagh. 'They buy and sell on the basis of the weather conditions.' Marks and Spencer take forecasts from Lynagh to assist them with fresh food distribution. 'Their buyers make decisions about what fresh goods they will put on their shelves, on the basis of our forecasts. If we get the forecast wrong it can cost the company several thousand pounds in one week. On one day when we predicted that it would be a very sunny Saturday, the rain came about 12 hours earlier than we had predicted and the company was left with something like £400 000 worth of salad goods unsold.'

Brewers would like forecasts three or four weeks ahead so that they have time to brew extra lager for a summer heatwave. But that so far eludes the forecasters. Film makers, builders and people who work outdoors need accurate forecasts. The Central Electricity Generating Board takes weather forecasts every hour. It needs to predict demand for power as accurately as possible because, while it costs a huge amount to generate electricity, there is no practical way of storing any excess. Unsold electricity is lost instantly. And since it also takes some time to bring a new generator on to the national grid, the better the board's weather forecasts the less electricity it wastes.

The trouble is that the weather is very unpredictable, especially in western Europe where our skies are a battleground between four different air masses. Two come from polar regions, one from Scandinavia and Siberia and the other from the North Atlantic. And two more come from the south: one from Africa and southern Europe, the other from the tropical Atlantic Ocean. The dominance of any one air mass will bring very different weather from the others. Most of our weather is created by the front, or boundary, between the northern and southern maritime air masses. Low pressure zones form along the front and ride towards Britain on westerly winds that are created by the spin of the earth on its axis. The southern air, bringing with it heat from the tropics, rises over the cold polar air, creating rainfall along the front. The fronts are responsible for most of Britain's rainfall. That is why most forecasts are for 'showers and sunny periods' and the outlook is always 'changeable'.

Predicting the movement of these fronts and the intensity of the storms that form along them is impossible for more than a few days ahead. So meteorologists, including those at Britain's Met Office, have tried from time to time to look for patterns that hold good on longer timescales. When Baur made his forecasts for Hitler, he was relying on theories about the weather and on charts, which enabled him to predict that if, for instance, it was sunny in Potsdam in July then it would be mild in Moscow in October. He reckoned that since there had been two harsh winters in Russia in a row, then it was due for a mild winter in 1941. Baur came unstuck because the weather has no memory. And the Met Office, which like Baur relied for its long-range forecasts on the idea that past patterns repeat themselves, abandoned these forecasts a decade ago. It concluded that they produced no better result than rolling a die.

Physicists describe the weather as a 'chaotic system' because small events can sometimes have huge and unpredictable consequences. It means that if the circumstances were right, the flap of a butterfly's wing in Tokyo or the breaking of a twig in the Amazon rainforest could produce a storm in Britain three weeks later. This is why, however good computer models of our climate become, it still remains almost impossible to predict British weather more than a few days ahead.

Alan Robock explains our predicament. 'You turn on the television and see a weather forecast that says it is going to rain a couple of days from now, but then it does not rain. Why was the forecast wrong? The answer is that the storm that was set to bring the rain may have gone in a slightly different direction or may have become a bit stronger or weaker than was forecast. This natural variability is happening all the time. When storms are stronger, they transport more heat from the equator to the polar regions. The temperature difference is what draws the storms. Because storms are unstable and can grow rapidly in a few days, they are unpredictable.'

The inherent unpredictability of climatic systems is always there to trip up meteorologists. Despite their sophistication, they conspicuously failed to spot, just a few hours in advance, a small twitch on a front approaching Europe from the Atlantic that rapidly produced the hurricane force winds of the 'great storm' that blasted through southern England in October 1987.

It was in this game of Russian roulette with the weather that Group Captain J. M. Stagg, the chief meteorologist for the D-day landings in Normandy in June 1944, successfully predicted four days in advance a brief gap in a long succession of storms during which the landings could take place. His forecast sealed Germany's fate in the Second World War. The following day, a serious storm blew up in the English Channel that would have wrecked the enterprise. Meteorologists to this day are impressed by Stagg's feat. In the war of the weathermen, Britain won hands down.

The requirements of war have meant that meteorologists have for many years had a strong involvement with national military authorities. It was no accident that central London's weather used always to be reported from the Air Ministry's roof. The needs of military aircraft have been the single biggest reason for the growth in weather forecasting. The link long predates the Battle of Britain, however. In the First World War, when poison gas was first used as a battlefield weapon, meteorologists were crucial figures in warning when the gas might blow back and poison the 'home side'.

It was immediately after that war that Britain's Meteorological Office became part of the military. A certain tension has persisted between the weather forecasters and the military ever since. The most revered British meteorologist, Lewis Richardson, who in 1922 wrote a book on how to use numerical systems (later reinvented as computers) to forecast the weather, was a Quaker and worked during the First World War as an ambulance driver taking victims of gas from the front. After the war, the military asked Richardson to do research into the diffusion of poison gases. He refused and resigned to teach physics at a small school in Scotland.

Climate of diplomacy

Co-operation between the weather forecasters of different countries has prospered. Data from weather stations on the ground, from ships, from the 600 balloons launched into the upper atmosphere every 12 hours round the world, and even some data from satellites are all shared by the international meteorological com-

At war with the weather. Hitler's march on Moscow was halted by Arctic conditions: however a break in the weather ensured success for the D-Day landings in 1944.

munity. They are united as they try to make sense of random events around them, to find the critical flapping butterfly's wing that may change weather round the globe.

Robock says that 'at the height of the Cold War, the USA, the Soviet Union and China exchanged weather data, even when they didn't have any diplomatic relations. Only during wartime are such links severed. For instance, just before Argentina attacked the Falkland Islands they sent a message on their computer link to Britain which claimed that they had computer problems and so were unable to send weather data.' In that instance the USA provided data for Britain from its satellites to make up for the lost ground-based data from Argentina.

It is distressing that the advent of weather satellites may reduce co-operation among meteorologists, because the richer nations will no longer be dependent on data collected in smaller nations.

CHAPTER 2

Storm cones

Storms come in all shapes and sizes and can be immensely destructive. There is growing concern that the tropical varieties in particular may become far more frequent and even more dangerous in a hotter, greenhouse world. In Britain, where our weather is usually made up of bits of everything but few extreme events, damaging storms may become more frequent. Even today they are not as rare as is often supposed. Michael Fish was the unfortunate BBC weather man who told the nation a couple of days before the 'great storm' of 1987: 'I've had a lady on the telephone who asks me if there is going to be a hurricane. I can assure her that there is not.' He spoke as if such things never happen in Britain. And in a sense he was right, since hurricanes are exclusively tropical formations requiring hot ocean waters to feed them. What blew Britain sideways that night was technically an explosive cyclone, a devastatingly virulent twitch on one of the long stream of fronts that bring most of our rain. The winds were of *hurricane force* in places, but that is different—a point understandably lost on a nation that felt let down by its weather service.

The classic damaging storm in Britain came in 1703, almost at the height of the little ice age. It was documented in detail by Daniel Defoe and makes recent events seem small. Some 8000 people died in this storm, and Defoe himself counted 17 000 trees uprooted in Kent and some 100 churches with their roofs stripped of lead before he gave up the task.

Fish's opposite number at ITV, Trish Williamson, says that the uniqueness of the 1987 storm may be an invention of southerners. 'People living in Sheffield in 1962 will remember a very, very severe storm and in 1968 in Glasgow I think nine people lost their lives, something like 17 000 people were left homeless and about 100 000 homes were damaged. I think there was a bit of bias from the media in 1987 because it was in the south of England.'

One peculiar type of storm is the tornado one of the still true climatic mysteries. Tornadoes are tiny and very destructive and form when warm air on a hot day suddenly rises quickly from the land, sometimes dragging objects from the ground with it and generating wind speeds of up to 200 miles per hour. They are most frequent in tropical areas, but occasionally form over Britain. 'In 1978,' says Williamson, 'there was a series of a dozen tornadoes moving across parts of Cambridgeshire towards the east coast. They were associated with a cold front.'

The nearest that most British get to understanding the power of tornadoes to suck things into the air and despatch them far away is the story of the Wizard of Oz. But during the Cambridgeshire tornadoes, says Williamson, '136 geese just fell dead out of the cloud as one of these tornadoes went by.' However, this pales into insignificance beside the American tornadoes. 'I walked out of my shop and then the tornado hit me,' said one Kansas victim. 'When I came round I was sitting over there and my shop had vanished. I lost my right arm and left leg.' In all, that tornado killed 46 people and did $8 million worth of damage.

Storms have played their part in shaping Europe, especially around the North Sea. The island of Heligoland in the German Bight, which was once owned by Britain, is now only a fortieth the size that it was 1000 years ago, because of the constant battering of storms. One day in 1694 a storm swept across the Culbin Estate on the south side of the Moray Firth in Scotland covering some 80 square kilometres of farmland with sand. According to Hubert Lamb formerly at the Climatic Research Unit, 'they were in the middle of the barley harvest. They retreated a bit and when it eased went back to carry on with the harvesting, but found that their ploughs had been buried. And that night their houses were buried with sand so that they had to evacuate their homes. The land was useless until the 1920s when somebody succeeded in getting trees to grow.'

This was at the height of the little ice age, when the North Sea experienced many storms that have had long-term consequences. The IJsselmeer, or Zuider Zee, drained at massive cost by the Dutch this century, was first inundated then. So were the Norfolk Broads. Storms destroyed two British ports: Ravenspur, which stood east of Hull beyond the present Spurn Point, and Dunwich on the coast of Suffolk. Perhaps most momentous of all was the devastating storm that struck the Spanish Armada in 1588, wrecking most of its ships off the west coat of Britain. Lamb has analysed many of these events in work paid for by oil companies, who are anxious to investigate the history of storms in the North Sea to help design oil platforms that can survive the worst that the sea can throw at them.

Seeds of success

The Reverend Pat Robertson, an American TV preacher who ran for the Republican presidential nomination in 1988, claimed during the campaign to have redirected a hurricane through prayer. The claim did not do his campaign much good, but American scientists believe that they may be able to do the same. The basis for their confidence is an extensive experiment called Project Storm Fury. This uses the principles of cloud seeding for producing rain. Planes fly into clouds where they drop tiny particles, usually of silver iodide, into the clouds. The particles act as nuclei around which raindrops form. In Project Storm Fury, the creation of rain was only a byproduct of their aim. The pilots seeded clouds just outside the eye of the hurricane, where the winds are strongest. 'If you can seed the clouds and make

Long range weather forecasts could allow brewers to produce more lager for a summer heatwave: (top right)however, six hour forecasts sometimes prove beyond meteorologists, as the Great Storm of October 1987 demonstrated.

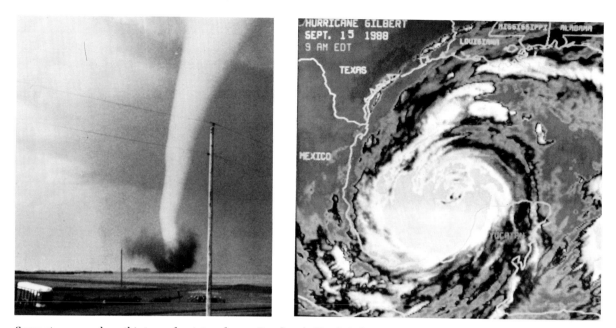

Some storms, such as this tornado pictured near Osnabrook, North Dakota, in 1978, bring only destruction, whereas others are also a source of rain. Hurricane Gilbert, which brought devastation to the Caribbean in 1988, beached the ship pictured below at Cancun in Mexico, but also brought welcome relief to the country's crops.

it rain that will take the energy out of those winds and make the eye bigger, and then the maximum winds will be less,' says Alan Robock.

Playing with hurricanes is dangerous, he says. What if something goes wrong? You could be saddled with a bill for billions of dollars of damage. Since most of the American hurricanes start life in the Caribbean, the political complications could be great, too. 'What if we had seeded a cloud and the hurricane had all of a sudden turned and gone right over Havana?' It would be largely immaterial whether the seeding caused the change in direction or not. The suspicion would be sufficient to cause a major international row.

The pilots who flew on missions for Project Storm Fury had strict instructions, recalls Robock. 'You had to fly out far enough from land so that if something went screwy and the hurricane turned it wouldn't come over land. They did seed a couple of hurricanes, which changed slightly after the seeding. But then for several years there were no hurricanes in the right place and the project finally stopped.'

Lou Grant, professor of atmospheric sciences at Colorado State University, remembers those experiments in the Caribbean as producing substantial evidence that seeding could reduce the strength of winds. But the effect was temporary and wind speeds increased again rather rapidly, once seeding ended. Indeed, the seeding may merely have prolonged the life of the hurricane.

As the result of the political and legal concern over seeding hurricanes in the Caribbean, the US National Weather Service attempted further experiments in the Pacific Ocean, flying planes from bases in the Philippines. 'There were great objections to these experiments from the Japanese and Chinese,' says Grant. Unlike those in the Caribbean, their concern was that the seeding might diminish the hurricanes. 'They depend for a substantial amount of their rainfall on hurricanes,' says Grant. So do many other countries in tropical regions. For them, the destructive power of tropical storms is just the flipside of beneficial rainfall. Parts of Mexico were devastated by Hurricane Gilbert in 1988, for instance. But the country depends on hurricanes for up to half its rain. In a lesser way, the same is true of Britain. In summer many of the rain-bearing depressions that pass over Britain, preventing droughts, began life as hurricanes in the Caribbean.

Grant has taken part in experiments for cloud seeding's other task: making rainfall to counter drought. Snow falling in the state of Colorado, where Grant works, provides most of the headwaters for the Colorado River, which runs the length of the arid American West, from the snow-covered mountains of Colorado through the desert state of Arizona to Mexico and the Pacific Ocean. Along the way, its waters are used repeatedly, to irrigate fields and to provide water for desert cities such as Phoenix and Tucson.

Most of the water once flowed down the river in a great rush in May and June, when the Colorado snowpack thawed. The parched lands through which the river passes needed reservoirs to hold the water. It is a boast of the engineers who tamed the river with the Hoover dam and a string of others that it was 'water that won the West', rather than the gun. But the water is now all spoken for and demand continues to grow, especially from California. Despite record flows in the Colorado in the mid-1980s, a snow drought in the winter of 1988–89 revived fears that the greenhouse effect could reduce flows by up to 50 per cent within a few decades. That could spell catastrophe for the American West, unless the rainmakers can wring extra snow from the clouds which blow in off the Pacific and over the Rockies.

'Weather modification could be very important to arid areas like the western USA,' say Grant. 'Here, the moisture comes in from the Pacific Ocean and is lifted up by the mountains. As it is lifted, it cools, clouds form and the clouds move rapidly over the mountains.' Only about 20 per cent of the water in those clouds falls as rain or snow. That is one reason why average precipitation in the Colorado Rockies is only 10 inches a year. The rest of the water in the clouds moves on over the mountains. And that is where Grant comes in. 'The concept of weather modification is to make more snow crystals faster so that a higher percentage of it will fall on the mountains,' he says.

Assuming that cloud seeding can be made to work, the big concern comes from people downwind, who say that if snow falls over the Rockies, then there will be less water vapour in the air to turn into rain that would fall further east. Grant disputes this view. He says that the water vapour that passes on over the mountains today 'produces little or no precipitation in the eastern USA'. If it is not condensed out and precipitated when being lifted over mountains 3000 metres high, he reasons, then it is unlikely to be condensed out in large quantities at lower altitudes. Most of the moisture for rainfall in the eastern USA comes from the Gulf of Mexico, he says, much of it from those tropical storms.

Even if Grant is correct, the political repercussions from suspicion that rainfall has been stolen (and the impossibility of proving those suspicions false) dog prospects for cloud seeding. Robock recalls that during a major drought on the east coast of the USA in the 1960s, the state of Pennsylvania passed a law banning cloud seeding without the permission of state officials. It was widely believed that experiments in cloud seeding had caused the drought in the first place.

How does cloud seeding work? Grant explains what happens to clouds as they roll in off the the Pacific and rise over the Rockies. 'The little cloud droplets that form as air is lifted over the mountains are sub-cool—that is they, are way below freezing point but are too small to fall to the ground. They might fall 3 metres a day.' In the air stream there will also be tiny particles—dust or sulphate particles from the ocean. They will act as nuclei around which snow crystals can form. 'When you have a snow crystal in this field of little cloud droplets, that crystal can grow very rapidly by absorbing the little cloud droplets. It can become large enough to fall out much faster than droplets. On many occasions, there are not enough of these ice nuclei to form enough snow crystals to use all of these little cloud droplets. The concept of weather modification is to provide artificial ice nuclei so that more snow crystals will form and a greater proportion of the droplets will form precipitation over the mountains.'

Grant believes that sometimes his cloud seeding experiments have increased precipitation by up to 20 per cent. 'We believe that the percentage could be even larger if we had better technology and knew more. The biggest problem is the adequate distribution of artificial ice nuclei into the clouds. You've got to provide time for it to disperse and reach the right concentrations.'

For the time being, work to improve the techniques of seeding are in abeyance, however, because of pressure from states that fear that Grant and his colleagues could be stealing their rain, and because the Colorado reservoirs have been filled by heavy snowfalls during the 1980s, snowfalls so unusual that there have been numerous deaths in avalanches on the popular ski-slopes of Colorado.

Could techniques developed over the Colarado Rockies one day break droughts in the Sahel? That is a matter of intense controversy. 'We have advanced to the point where under the right conditions we can increase rainfall in mountain clouds,' says Grant. But different types of clouds present different problems. And you run the risk that you might put too many nuclei into a cloud and create too many snow crystals. Then, none of them would be able to grow large enough to fall out of the cloud as snow. Seeding could end up reducing rainfall.

Grant says that clouds that form over mountains are among the easiest to assess, largely because the physical consequences of the air rising over mountains of known height are easy to calculate. Other types of clouds, such as those formed by hot air rising on a sunny afternoon (so-called convective clouds) are much more complex. 'We do not yet understand those clouds sufficiently,' says Grant, 'to be able to modify the weather effectively'.

'The Sahel in North Africa has large convective clouds. There's been no research done on those clouds but I would suspect that there would be times when you could increase precipitation, times when you couldn't, and times when you really don't know the difference.'

Even with the research done, he believes, cloud seeding 'would be no panacea that would solve the drought. You've got to have cloud, you've got to have the moisture and you've got to have the right kind of cloud.' You certainly cannot make it rain out of a cloudless sky.

Many climatologists are much more sceptical about the possibilities of cloud seeding. Reid Bryson says that in most parts of the world there are already plenty of ice nuclei in the clouds and extra ones will have little effect. 'In general, in places like the Midwestern USA or in Europe there is enough stuff in the air already that adding more isn't going to help,' he says.

Robock is equally cautious. 'It has actually been demonstrated only in one place, in Israel, that in clouds that form over mountains, you can get a bit more rainfall by seeding them. And there is a big question about whether cloud seeding can work in convective clouds and in thunderstorm clouds.'

Maybe this is scientific caution. In the all-too-real world of warfare, weather modification has been attempted, though with what success it is hard to gauge. During the Vietnam war from 1966 to 1972, the CIA seeded the clouds over the

Ho Chi Minh trail, a path through Laos that the North Vietnamese used to supply guerrilla fighters in South Vietnam. The aim of the seeding was to extend the rainy season. 'They thought that it would be muddier, make it harder for the Vietcong to bring the supplies in. None of our spies had rain gauges so we don't really know whether it worked,' says Robock.

There have also been reports of attempts to modify weather in North Vietnam to upset enemy radar used to aim defensive missile systems and to help bombing missions. The Stockholm International Peace Research Institute estimated that the USA made a total of more than 2600 flights with planes equipped to seed clouds during the Vietnam War, but it too is sceptical about whether they had much success. The USA also once seeded clouds in the Caribbean in an attempt to make them rain before reaching Cuba and so ruin the Cuban sugar crop. 'That year the harvest was actually less than normal,' says Robock, 'but it's difficult to prove whether those activities caused it.'

More recently there have been claims in the Soviet Union that, after the Chernobyl nuclear accident, scientists seeded clouds coming from the area. They feared that radioactive material would contaminate clouds and fall on Moscow. To avoid this, according to a letter in the Young Communist newspaper, *Komsomolskya Pravda*, the clouds were seeded so that the fall-out landed on villages in the Mogilev region of Byelorussia. Whether the seeding worked is unclear. But we do know to our cost that Lapland, Scotland and the Lake District were all eventually contaminated by radioactivity borne on winds from the east and rained over Britain.

City rain

If human success in altering the weather deliberately seems limited, there is no doubt that we are inadvertently modifying the weather quite substantially. Air pollution can change clouds dramatically, for instance. It is well known that sulphur and nitrogen pollution can turn rain acid. But tiny particles of sulphate in that acid pollution may themselves seed clouds. They mimic natural sulphate particles from marine organisms, which appear to be the most important cloud nuclei in many parts of the world.

Smoke pollution in urban areas is a cause of fog. From Victorian times until the early 1960s London was notorious for its pea-souper smogs. A blanket of warm air above the capital trapped cold air close to the ground for days on end. The fog that formed beneath this 'temperature inversion' became polluted by the smoke. The word 'smog' was coined. After clean-air legislation cut the pollution, meteorologists noticed that the fogs disappeared along with the pollution. It appeared that the smoke was itself helping to sustain the inversion layer by preventing the sun's rays from reaching the ground and heating up the bottom layer of the atmosphere.

We have already mentioned the urban heat-island effect in which asphalt and buildings store heat, particularly at night. One important effect of the urban heat

Smoke from domestic fires helped perpetuate London smogs. 4000 people died in the smog of 1952, shown here at midday in Trafalgar Square.

island is to intensify storm clouds by changing the humidity of the air over the city and supplying the clouds with extra heat. This tends to increase rainfall downwind of cities. Studies around Chicago, the USA's third largest city, and St Louis have both shown the effect of such 'heat shadows' in action.

Soviet scientists have noticed that the Moscow heat island causes passing snow clouds to dump their load on the city. So they have attempted to seed clouds approaching Moscow in winter, so that the snow falls before it reaches the city. They say that rising warm air from the Moscow heat island actually draws storm clouds towards the city. When the clouds arrive, the rising air forces the clouds higher, making more water vapour in them freeze and so seeding the formation of snow crystals and ultimately snowfall.

Even farming can change the weather. The widespread irrigation of crops appears to change the climate in parts of the arid American West. Water in reservoirs, canals and in the surface layers of the soil can all evaporate into the air, providing extra moisture from which new clouds can form. The result appears to be more rainfall in western Texas, western Kansas and Nebraska, says Lou Grant.

CHAPTER 3

The desiccation of Africa

One of the greatest challenges to humanity in the 1980s has been our response to the drought-prone lands of Africa. Live Aid brought home to the world the human suffering in countries such as Ethiopia, Sudan and many other countries from Mauritania in the northwest to Mozambique in the southeast. But, generous as individuals round the world have proved in the face of suffering, the world's response has been weakened by uncertainty about the nature of the crisis. Is it economic: poor countries unable to make their way in a wicked world? Political: corrupt regimes wracked by civil wars incapable of responding to the most basic needs of their citizens? Environmental: too many people chopping down too many trees, over-farming fields and over-grazing pastures and causing massive ecological degradation? Climatic: shifting weather systems triggering shifting sands?

The answer is undoubtedly all four, with different emphases in different places at different times. But the evidence of climatic change is growing very strong. Until a respite in 1988, the African Sahel, a region of dry land stretching along the southern edge of the Sahara desert, had experienced two decades of almost continual below-average rainfall. Within that overall decline, there were two major droughts, in the early 1970s (when up to 250 000 people may have died) and the early 1980s, with a smaller drought in 1987. The decline in rainfall has been mirrored in other tropical desert regions, from the Rajasthan desert in northwest India to Mexico and northeastern Brazil, where hunger forced many refugees to head for the Amazon rainforest in the mid-1980s.

Mick Kelly at the Climatic Research Unit believes that there is a global change in climate at work here and that the root cause could be the early stages of the greenhouse effect. His colleague, Jean Palutikof, says that 'as the drought persists from year to year, more and more climatologists are coming round to the view that this is true. Almost none of them are prepared, quite reasonably, to put it in writing. If we all sat down and said that there's a drought in the Sahel and that it is going to go on indefinitely because it is greenhouse-induced, it would suddenly start to rain and we'd all look very stupid.'

Some would argue that a few heavy rainstorms over Khartoum, the capital of Sudan, in September 1988 did indeed make the greenhouse theory of the Sahel drought look stupid. But Palutikof disagrees. 'One thing that climatologists seem to be fairly sure about is that the climate will not just change steadily in one direction.

It will become more variable, more stormy, more uncertain. So those storms could be a sign of what might happen next in the Sudan—that these very sudden, very destructive rainstorms may become more common in future.' Such storms will be of little use to agriculture, she says. 'If you are going to receive all your annual rainfall in one huge destructive storm, then most of the water will run off into rivers and very little will go into the soil.'

The understandable timidity of researchers to declare their fears that the green-house effect may be causing the Sahelian drought has resulted in important science being left undone, Palutikof believes. 'We were very foolish not to put a lot of scientists into the Sahel to do research to see how human societies reacted to such a marked climatic change. It's quite likely that all of us are going to have to go through similar convulsive changes over the next 20–40 years, and we have no feel for how we are going to be able to respond to those changes. We could have seen something in the Sahel about how resilient people can be, but we didn't take the opportunity. We should be on our toes to make sure that we don't miss the next, wherever that may be.'

Evidence of the impact of past climate changes litters the Sahara. Cave paintings from Tassili in the heart of the desert, which today is lifeless, show lions, hippos, trees and even boats. The pictures were drawn some 6000 years ago, when the monsoons were more intense and the region was far wetter. The desert then was covered by grass. Elephants and giraffes roamed as far north as Algeria. The present desert was a paradise for neolithic fishermen. At that time Lake Chad, in the centre of the current desert, covered 350 000 square kilometres, about the size of the present-day Caspian Sea. Today, though it still drains an area approaching the size of the USA, Lake Chad is less than a hundredth of its former size.

The climate became drier from about 5000 years ago, in one of the sudden disruptive changes identified by Reid Bryson. Some of the history of the drying of the Sahara and surrounding areas is revealed in the Old Testament, says Hubert Lamb. It turns up, for instance, 'in the wanderings of Abraham (and even Moses in later centuries), trying to find land to settle in where the climate would be reliable enough to allow agricultural settlement. It was an uphill struggle against a world that was becoming more hostile.' The Saharan climate changed largely because of a decline in the west African monsoon and because the tracks of storms bringing clouds and rain from the Atlantic moved north. Today, those storms may be on the move again, drying out the Sahara yet more.

Deserts exist on the edge of the tropics on each continent around the world, both north and south of the equator. In Africa there is the Sahara and the Kalahari desert; in the Americas the desert region of the southwestern USA and northern Mexico and the dry lands of Peru and Chile in the south; then there is the Rajasthan desert in India, as well as western Australia. In these dry lands, some 600 million people maintain an often precarious existence.

The deserts form because of one of the basic features of the world's climatic system. At the equator, intense warming from the overhead sun makes the air rise.

As it rises it cools, the moisture it contains falls as rain, creating the damp conditions in which rainforests thrive. But having cooled and discarded its moisture, the air sinks back to the earth's surface, creating a zone of intense dryness. Many researchers believe that as the world warms under the influence of the greenhouse effect, the tropical rainmaking machine may become more vigorous and that as a paradoxical result, the desert zones on the fringes of the tropics, such as the Sahara, may intensify and spread. If that happens, the dry marginal lands where today many millions of people live on the threshold of drought could become desert. And passably wet areas (on which much of the world depends for grain crops) could become dry and increasingly drought-prone.

During the 1950s and 1960s, when the world appeared to be taking a breather in its gradual process of warming, the climate in the Sahel was unusually benign. Rainfall was above average. This coincided with a population boom that persuaded farmers to take their ploughs out into the desert margins. And beyond where the fields stopped, herdsmen extended their herds of cattle and flocks of goats. When the crisis came in the 1970s, farmers responded to declining crop yields by annexing even more marginal land for cultivation. But the nomadic herdsmen, without access to the land they had once resorted to in times of drought, often slaughtered their emaciated animals and headed for refugee camps or the cities. The Tuareg, for instance, were one of the most independent of the Sahara's nomadic groups. But today most have joined the swelling shanty towns attached to the capital cities of neighbouring countries, such as Nouakchott in Mauritania and Monrovia in Liberia.

Mirages

The evidence that the greenhouse effect may be linked to the drying of the Sahara is compelling. But there may be other causes. One is the destruction by humans of vegetation in the countries around the Sahel. Most of coastal west Africa—countries such as Liberia, Ghana and the Ivory Coast—was once covered by rainforest. Today more than two-thirds of the forests have gone. Inland, too, verdant grass and scrublands have been replaced by dusty fields. All vegetation, but forests in particular, help create rain. Forests and their soils act as a giant sponge for water falling from clouds as they blow inland from the sea. Up to half the water may be re-evaporated into the air from the leaves of the trees. It can then blow further inland, where it will fall as rain once more. But if the trees are removed, then the coastal rainfall flows straight into the soil (which it may erode) and into rivers and back to the sea. There is no evaporation to produce rain further inland. Many believe that this process is a prime reason for the drying out of the Sahel.

Another could be dust. Reid Bryson believes that dust is one of the under-estimated factors in the world's climate. He says 'one of the things that happens when you devegetate a region is that you make it easier for the wind to blow dust around'. Researchers have indeed spotted a marked increase in the amount of

Saharan dust on the move round the world. It is responsible for the increasing amount of 'red rain' in Britain, when red dust from the Sahara falls from the skies. Here the dust is a novelty. In the Sahel it may stop rain from falling. Most rain in the Sahel falls at night, says Bryson, when the tops of the clouds cool, making them unstable. But a layer of dust above the clouds would act like a blanket and prevent that cooling.

Since the 1970s it has become fashionable to believe that the Sahara is spreading and that the root cause of this and of the famines is the degradation of the land itself, by farming or cattle rearing that is too intense to be sustainable. Workineh Degefu from the Ethiopian National Meteorological Service says: 'I think deserts are a creation of human activities. The unbalanced use of land where the potential to use exceeds what man puts in causes desertification.' In years when rainfall is poor, he says, farmers try to carry on as normal and, as a result, 'remove the green cover from the soil'. Once the soil is exposed, wind erosion sets in and, when the rains return, they too erode the top soil, decreasing its fertility and increasing the pressure on farmers to over-cultivate their soils. 'Even if the rainfall returns to normal, once the fertility is removed the process of desertification continues.'

This pessimistic analysis is what lies behind the insistence of the Ethiopian government that the people of the drought-stricken northern highlands, the province of Wollo and several others, which became distressingly famous a few years ago, must be moved to new lands in the south of the country to allow the highlands to 'rehabilitate'. But investigators are beginning to believe that the analysis wrong. It makes no allowance, they say, for the powers of recovery of the natural ecosystems. Lennart Olsson, a geographer from the University of Lund in Sweden, says, 'When we carried out surveys among the farmers in Sudan and asked them about what desertification is, they replied that it is just the lack of rain. Most scientists have just laughed at them. But I think now we can say that they were right.'

Many visitors to Ethiopia are struck by the suddenness with which the parched land turns green at the first rainfall after a dry spell. They had assumed that the dirt in front of them showed that the land had been reduced to desert. But, says Olsson, 'dry areas have enormous resilience ... when the conditions go back to normal the vegetation will come back again. We can compare this with the bare ground in front of a goal on a football field. There is no grass, because players have been running round there a lot, but the soil is still able to produce good and green grass.' Researchers today are questioning the accepted wisdom that 'overgrazing' of grasslands by the herds of nomads is an ecological disaster for the dry lands of Africa.

Even data on the spread of deserts often turn out, on close inspection, to be seriously flawed. One study widely quoted by the UN's experts on desertification misleading compared the edge of the dry lands between an extremely wet year (1958), when the desert margins would have been lush, with observations made in 1974, in the final stages of an intense drought. In 1974, says Olsson, the UN's researcher 'flew over parts of the Sudan in a couple of days, trying to define the desert boundary from an airplane. Then he compared his boundary with a vegetation map of the Sudan made in 1958, and there was a 100-kilometre discrepancy between the two maps.' It turns out, says Olsen, that the 1958 map was made not by inspecting the desert, but by drawing a line on a map where rainfall appeared to be less than 75 millimetres a year, which is one definition of a desert. In other words, the data from the two maps were not comparable. This 'quick and dirty' study, as Olsen calls it, turns out to have been the basis for the repeated claims—made again in 1988 by George Bush—that the Sahara is advancing at a rate of 6 kilometres a year. The truth is that nobody knows if it is advancing or not.

Almost all the popular conceptions about spreading deserts are false, says Olsen. 'The most common images of desertification are that the desert, in the form of mobile sand dunes, is moving and covering fertile land; that this is caused purely by man; and that once you have lost the productivity of the land it is irreversible. I think we can say that all these three popular images are wrong. In fact, the deserts are stable. Food production is almost totally controlled by fluctuations in rainfall. And we can see that arid zone ecosystems are extremely resilient.'

A good example of this is in north Africa where 1988 saw the best harvest for 20 years, says Olsson, only two years after one of their worst droughts. 'That's a very good argument for there being no irreversible processes.'

Faulty analysis of the kind highlighted by Olsson has damaging consequences for desert farmers. The idea of irreversible ecological decline, Olsson says, meant that 'the UN and the World Bank thought that desertification was such a threat [to the arid countries of Africa] that they didn't dare to fund any projects in those countries because they thought they were about to be turned into desert. They were more or less lost areas.' More recent assessments by the World Bank, however, have contributed to the new thinking and the bank 'now recommends aid organisations to give support to dry countries'.

Another frequent consequence of the conventional wisdom has been for governments to pen nomadic herders into ever smaller areas, because ministers believe that their cattle are destroying the land. 'It's my experience,' says Palutikof, 'that people who live in that kind of society are much more careful of their environment. You read about people grazing goats and sheep and cutting down trees and being generally wasteful. But not one of these trees will have been cut down for a frivolous reason. All this talk about "overgrazing" as far as I am concerned is just garbage.' Where problems do arise, she says, they are usually failures of external agencies, such as government attempts to control the nomads.

The idea that the dunes are on the move has led aid agencies to spend many millions of pounds on planting trees in the desert in an effort to hold them back. Yet few sand dunes do move in the Sahara. 'There was no desert to stop,' says Olsson. 'Planting trees in the desert is a popular form of aid because it is something visual. A green tree surrounded by sand dunes is a very good picture to show to all the supporters back home in Europe.'

This is not to decry the virtues of planting trees in places where people will use

Demand for firewood (see over) is destroying forests in many developing countries.

As the trees disappear, so may the soil.

them. Trees provide fuel, wood, shelter and construction materials. But if the incentive is there, people will plant trees for themselves. The most important tree in many parts of Sudan is the acacia, which produces gum arabic, common glue. 'It is one of the most important export products from the Sudan,' says Olsson. 'Over many years the production of gum arabic decreased because the price was so low that there was no incentive for farmers to pick it. It paid better to fell the trees and cultivate the land. But recently the Sudanese government increased the price to the farmers by 100 per cent and we can see an immediate response. Suddenly there were trees everywhere ... We can compare this with an aid organisation spending millions of pounds planting trees.'

Olsson sees this market approach to developing poor dry countries as a great improvement on the attitude of the Ethiopean government, outlined by Degefu whose aim is to 'inventorise' Ethiopia's natural resources, including its soils, and to 'design a land-use policy appropriate to the land's potential. Each land or area should be used in accordance to what it can provide.' In some places this will involve 'removing the people' to allow a forest to be planted or to let soils recover.

Tequila sunset

Tucson, Arizona, is in the heart of the desert. But this is no famine-ridden desert. It is the affluent American sunbelt, close to the Mexican border, where the rich from the east go to retire to their golf courses and sip their cocktails, and where the sunrise industries of computers and aerospace congregate. It is almost obscene to compare Tucson with the arid regions of the Sahel. Enough water evaporates from the average backyard swimming pool in Tucson to make the difference between life and death for a destitute Ethiopian family. Whole herds of Sudanese cattle could thrive on the well-watered golf courses that litter the town. But in its way it is a sign of hope for the poor arid lands of the world. The problem for the Sudanese and Ethiopian people is not the desert so much as their poverty.

Money, for the moment, can buy Tucson water as well as life's other essentials. But Tucson is on a knife-edge. It is the largest city in the world without a regular supply of surface water. Its 300 000 people tap into diminishing supplies of 'fossil water' underground. The water table, the highest point in the ground from which the water can be drawn, used to be 2 metres below the surface, but today it is often 60 metres. Water that took hundreds of years to accumulate is being sprayed on to golf courses. So Tucson is looking for new sources of water. It is now helping pay the $5 billion bill to bring water by canal from the Colorado River into the heart of the Arizona desert. And in the market economy for water, the irrigated farms may have to yield their supplies.

Despite urban profligacy, 85 per cent of the water consumed in Arizona still goes to irrigate farmland such as cotton fields. But many fertile valleys are no longer farmed because the cost of pumping water from deep underground for irrigation is

79

Will planting trees, shown here on the edge of the Sahara, hold back advancing sand dunes?

too high for the farmers. So city councils in the region now regularly buy up farms and shut them down in order to take over their water rights.

Chuck Stockton of the University of Arizona works in Tucson but is also an adviser for the Moroccans who, in a similar physical environment to Arizona but a very different economic one, want to make the best use of their desert lands. Stockton believes that there are lessons to be learned from Tucson. Crops developed at his university to survive in dry and often salty soils in Arizona transfer well to Morocco, he says. 'Many areas of Morocco look identical to parts of Arizona,' and we think that our technology can be readily transferred there.' This is the kind of high-tech approach to arid farming also being developed in Israel. It may not be appropriate to the needs of rural communities throughout Africa, but it shows that 'desertified' lands should not be written off. They, and Africa, still have great potential to fulfil. Tucson, home of Biosphere II and some of the world's most expensive water, may hold some of the keys to survival in the global greenhouse.

CHAPTER 4

A cancer in the planet's 'lung'

The destruction of the Amazon rainforest is one of the great environmental disasters of our time. It is potentially a catastrophe for the environment and climate of Brazil—and a major jolt to the whole planet. Ghillean Prance, director of Kew Botanical Gardens, is trying to unravel the secrets of the Amazon rainforest before it is all gone. 'The Amazon is being decimated,' he says. 'In 1988, over 90 000 square kilometres were burned down. I looked at satellite photographs of Rondonia, a state in the west of the Amazon basin, and saw 6800 fires burning in a single day. We're not exaggerating when we say that areas as large as the UK are disappearing in a single year now in the Amazon. It is terrible.'

Brazil claims that, while the worst excesses of destruction must be tamed, the country needs the land that is presently under forest to aid its economic development. Late in 1988, in a concession to world opinion, the Brazilian government abolished the tax incentives that encouraged people to invade the rainforest. And in early 1989 a 'special programme for the Amazon', called Our Nature, was launched. Apart from being a clear attempt to reassert its right to decide what happens in the Amazon region, the government intends that the programme will help to 'incorporate the Amazon' into the Brazilian economy while 'conserving the forest and protecting the natural resources'. This aim is laudable, but extremely vague, considering that friends of the Amazon rainforest, such as Prance, believe that fundamental changes in policy will be necessary before the government's professed desire to support 'sustainable development' of the region can be fulfilled.

The invasion of the Amazon is being carried out both by the landless poor (escaping from drought in north east Brazil and the shanty towns around São Paulo and Rio de Janeiro) and by mining companies and commercial cattle ranchers. The government is aiding the process by its policies towards the poor, by carving roads through the jungle and by flooding forested valleys to provide hydroelectric power for the mining and mineral-processing companies. And it is abetted by international finance institutions, led until recently by the World Bank, which now admits that its efforts to aid development in Rondonia and elsewhere have turned into an ecological disaster. Now Brazil is courting the Japanese.

Cattle ranching is a special scandal in the Amazon, and is devoid of economic logic. Says Prance: 'The beef that's made is second grade; the production is very low at one cow per hectare.' Most of the beef goes for domestic consumption rather than, as in Central America, to fill North American hamburgers.

The native Indian population, says Prance, 'is being driven back into the wild'. Some forest dwellers, however, are determined to fight. Chico Mendes, a rubber tapper who campaigned against the invading ranchers, was murdered in 1988. A demonstration of native Indians in the 'frontier town' of Altamira early in 1989 was organised with the help of foreign environmental groups to capture headlines round the world. And a few weeks later, the media were full of bizarre stories of an Indian 'chief' called Raoni, with a traditional lip plate, engaging in light-hearted banter about the destruction of the rainforest while accompanying the rock singer Sting on his European concert tour. Such antics, while highly successful in alerting the tabloid-reading world to the fate of the Amazon rainforest, angered the Brazilian government who threatened to refuse visas for scientists such as Prance wishing to document the biology of the region.

'Every year,' says Prance, 'species of plants are becoming extinct because some of the areas being colonised coincide with places containing unique plants. This is serious, not least because plants are useful things. The Arawak Indians use every single species of tree on a sample plot that we examined. And we don't know how many useful plants are hidden there. Only about 2 per cent of the total Amazon region has been analysed chemically. There may be undiscovered cures for cancer, AIDS and other human diseases in the plants of the Amazon and other rainforests of the world, and we're losing them before we've even had the change to name them or to study them chemically.'

These are not idle fears. A quarter of all the prescriptions made out in the USA are for chemicals derived from plants discovered in rainforests. They include curare, used by Indians as a tip for poisonous arrows but invaluable in the developed world to relax muscles before surgery; quinine, which cures malaria; and pilocarpine, a treatment for glaucoma.

The tragedy of the destruction of the Amazon rainforest by farmers is that in many places it will destroy the very things that make farming there possible at present: the rainfall and the soils. As in Africa, much of the rain that falls inland is made possible by trees in coastal regions recycling moisture back into the air. Recent investigations have tracked the passage of rain from the Atlantic Ocean. It appears to make its way across the width of the continent in daily jumps, falling each time into the rainforest and then returning to the air to be blown further inland. Small-scale farming in the forest clearings, as practised for thousands of years by Indian communities, did not disrupt this process. But 'now they're taking out big areas of the forest,' says Prance. 'So the rain doesn't go any further in and you get reduced rainfall. The drier parts of the Amazon are becoming drier and that will begin to change the vegetation.'

There is a popular idea that the Amazon rainforest is some primeval forest, a planetary 'lung' without which our living planet will cease to function. This is a little way from the truth. 'It is a fallacy to say that the Amazon has been covered with forest for millions and millions of years,' says Prance. As recently as 20 000 years ago, during the last ice age, this 'lung' was reduced to puny proportions. Most of the land now occupied by forest was taken up by grassland and scrub. 'The forest was confined to smaller areas along the rivers.' Rainfall was much less at that time and, except where the rivers provided local sources of water, there was not enough rain in the heart of Amazonia to sustain the rainforest. It is an indication of what could happen as humans disrupt the Amazonian climate, reducing rainfall in the interior by eating away at the fringes of the forest.

The natural process of contraction was much less destructive than the present human activity, says Prance. The soil was not badly affected because there was always vegetation cover. So when the warmer climate came, it was much easier for the natural recolonisation of the forest. None the less, Prance believes that it is important to investigate these past changes because 'they are keys to understanding how we might conserve and how we might regenerate the Amazon when it is destroyed'. After the end of the last ice age, it took the Amazon rainforest about 6000 years to regrow. Without human intervention to speed the process, the damage already done by human activity will take about 1000 years to undo completely, he says.

What should be done to reverse the damage? First, says Prance, we must conserve threatened species by setting up reserves in the areas where there is the greatest genetic variety. But, he says, 'we can no longer expect the entire region to be kept pristine. The most important research priority is to find sustainable ways of using the Amazon rainforest,' systems that will not destroy soils or upset the forest's natural rain recycling machinery. 'Instead of going in and clearing the forest for cattle pasture we need something like agroforestry, in which trees are planted or retained along with crops. That way, Brazil could have the best of both worlds.'

Another priority, he says, is to find ways to put into productive use land that has already been degraded by farming activity. Despite the more horrendous prognoses for the Amazon, soils are not all irreparably destroyed when trees are removed. They decline in fertility and some may be eroded but much can be restored. 'Instead of leaving the abandoned cattle pastures to their fate,' says Prance, 'we should see what trees we can plant in them, find ways to turn the pastures back into useful forest.'

The fragile tropics

Governments in tropical countries point disparagingly at Western environmentalists and their governments, accusing them of hypocrisy for having torn down their forests to fuel economic development before chastising their poorer cousins for attempting the same. The moral case may be sound, suggests Prance, but the science is not. 'The tropics are so different from the temperate regions,' he says. 'Yes, we did chop down our trees, but we didn't lose the species because we had so

Ghillean Prance, Director of Kew Botanical Gardens, bemoans the wanton destruction of tropical rain forests such as the one pictured in Peru (below).

few species to lose. In the tropics, you get up to 300 species of trees in a single hectare. The diversity is so great and you get so many species that are found only in a small area.'

Also, the temperate lands 'have been blessed with fertile soils. Where we've removed forest, the agriculture has gone on from year to year. Although soil erosion is a serious problem in some places, particularly in the USA, by and large we have got away with it. About 80 per cent of the tropical forest is on such poor soil that it is just not appropriate for long term agricultural use. We should use the places where the soil is appropriate and recognise that forest uses are much better then deforestation.'

People who live off the forests in ways that do not destroy them—by harvesting rubber latex, Brazil nuts, tonka beans and the like—should be encouraged and their markets should be developed, says Prance. 'We also need to be assured that if we develop a drug from the rainforest that the profits go back to the country of origin as well as to the drug company that developed it. At Kew Gardens, we will not sign a contract with a drug company unless there is a royalty agreement both to our garden and to the country of origin, because we want to see the resources going back to where they began.'

While the Amazon rainforest is currently under most threat and receiving most international attention, many other tropical rainforests face destruction. The Pacific coast of Colombia and Ecuador, possibly the most genetically rich forest region in the world, is under intense threat. The Madagascan rainforests, a similarly unique environment, are mostly gone. And deforestation is proceeding apace in the Far Eastern countries of the Philippines and Malaysia. In Indonesia a programme to move millions of people from the crowded island of Java to larger, less populated islands is leading to wholesale destruction of forests in Borneo and western New Guinea.

Most of the forests of the Far East are cut down by farmers and supply the large world demand for hardwoods, especially in Japan. In Africa, most of the West African rainforest is gone and that leaves the vast rainforest of the Congo, after the Amazon the largest rainforest in the world and still largely untouched.

The loss of the world's rainforests is reducing the genetic diversity of our planet, as well as damaging local soils and climate and contributing to the growing menace of the greenhouse effect. Forests are a vast natural reservoir of carbon, which trees acquire by taking carbon dioxide from the atmosphere. There is roughly as much carbon in the trunks of trees and the soils of forests as there is in the atmosphere itself. Until perhaps the late 1950s, the destruction of forests—in temperate lands more than the tropics—was the single largest cause of the accumulation of carbon dioxide in the atmosphere. Whether the trees were burned or turned into paper or pit props or salad bowls, most of the carbon returned to the atmosphere within a few years or decades.

Today, the burning of fossil fuels has taken over as the main cause of the greenhouse effect, releasing 5–6 billion tonnes of carbon into the atmosphere each year. The destruction of tropical rainforests may add another 2 billion, though there is great uncertainty about the true figures. The extensive planting of commercial forests in other latitudes—from New England and Scotland to China and South Korea—has reduced the overall imbalance between carbon absorbed by and lost by the world's forests. The forests may now be near equilibrium, according to some estimates. But any future strategy for containing the greenhouse effect is likely to see forests as an important potential store for the unwanted carbon in the atmosphere. There is likely to be a major programme of planting new forests that can absorb the carbon dioxide. But before such a project makes sense, the international community is bound to want strict rules in countries such as Brazil to halt the wholesale destruction of the remaining natural forests.

Even if none of the local effects of the deforestation of the tropics is of any consequence, the global imperative to act against the greenhouse effect now requires an end to the carnage.

PART THREE

Models of the Future

CHAPTER 1

Greenhouse gases

Polar bears are not the most obvious victims of the greenhouse effect. But in November 1988 families of bears had their centuries-old patterns of migration across the Arctic ice disrupted. During the summer the bears range far into the Arctic in their search for food. As the winter sets in they move south towards their winter hibernation grounds. But last winter, for the first time in living memory, their passage was halted. The James Bay, a giant meteorite crater on the edge of the Hudson Bay in northern Canada, had failed to freeze. Driven by instinct, the bears made repeated hopeless bids to cross until the water froze a full six weeks late.

The bears were not alone in their confusion. The warm ice-free winter created gaping holes in the ice, which forced Sir Ranulph Twistleton Wickham Fiennes, a British explorer, to abandon his attempt to reach the North Pole on foot. What disrupted polar bears and an English explorer in the winter of 1988 could be playing havoc with much of the world within a few decades. That extraordinarily warm early winter in the Arctic could be an early consequence of the warming of our planet caused by the greenhouse effect. As warming intensifies in the coming decades, polar bears and walruses, stranded on thinning sheets of ice, may be among the first species to disappear.

A number of natural gases, known as 'greenhouse gases', form a warm blanket over the surface of the planet. Without them the planet would be too cold to support life. The most important greenhouse gas is carbon dioxide and changes in its concentration in the air seem to lie at the heart of all temperature changes on our planet, including (as we have seen), the ice ages. The most dramatic evidence of this has been revealed during the 1980s with the analysis by French scientists of pockets of air found in long cores of ice drilled by Soviet scientists from the ice pack of Antarctica at their research station called Vostock. The year-by-year record of concentrations of gases in the air provided by these ice cores goes back 160 000 years, through the most intense periods of two ice ages. It shows that the amount of carbon dioxide in the air varied almost exactly as the temperature varied.

In the depth of the last ice age, the concentration of carbon in the air was around 210 parts per million (ppm). By the late eighteenth century, on the eve of the industrial revolution, the level was about 270 ppm. Until that point almost all the changes in levels of carbon dioxide in the air could be attributed to natural

91

events. But after that humans began to take over, as first Britain, then Europe and North America and more recently China, India and other developing nations began rapid economic development based on burning cheap supplies of coal and oil and the demolition of forests to expand agriculture in an effort to feed their booming populations.

Between 1850 and 1914, emissions of carbon dioxide from burning fossil fuels rose by 4 per cent each year. From then to 1945, through two world wars and economic recessions, the rate fell to 1.5 per cent a year, before rising again to 4 per cent until 1973 and the first energy crisis, when the OPEC oil-producing nations quadrupled their prices overnight, sending world economies into recession. For a decade the rate of increase was a mere 1 per cent a year, but since 1985, a fall in oil prices has seen the use of fossil fuel begin to escalate again to about 2.5 per cent. In absolute terms the increase between 1985 and 1986 was the greatest ever recorded. The current output is around 5.6 billion tonnes of carbon a year, a little more than 1 tonne per head of the world's population.

Total emissions in the past 150 years have been about 200 billion tonnes, of which perhaps half remains in the air. At the same time, large amounts of carbon dioxide have been added to the air by the destruction of forests, adding anything between 100 and 200 billion tonnes. Estimates remain very uncertain, but forest destruction probably remained the most important source of extra carbon dioxide in the air until the 1950s and, even allowing for forest planting, may still contribute up to 2 billion tonnes a year.

The immediate effect of this pollution has been an increase in the concentration of carbon dioxide in the air from 270 ppm to 350 ppm, a landmark passed in 1988. If emissions increase for the next 40 years at a rate of 4 per cent a year, the annual emission could rise to 15 billion tonnes by 2030, roughly 2 tonnes per head of population, and the concentration in the air could exceed 500 ppm. Unless something happens to break the link between carbon dioxide and temperature, we can expect by then a world that is warmer by perhaps 4° or 5°C.

The effect will be compounded by the addition of other greenhouse gases. The main ones are methane and nitrous oxide from farming, and chlorofluorocarbons, artificial chemicals better known for the damage they are doing to the ozone layer. Between them, they now contribute as much to the enhanced greenhouse effect as carbon dioxide.

A whiff of marsh gas

The second most important greenhouse gas is methane, which currently causes about a fifth of the greenhouse effect. It is increasing in the atmosphere at a rate of more than 1 per cent a year. While levels of carbon dioxide are expected to have doubled their pre-industrial levels by about 2040, methane concentrations have already more than doubled. Many investigators, including a team from the USA's

National Center for Atmospheric Research at Boulder, Colorado, believe that within 50 years methane could be the number one greenhouse gas.

Most of the methane in the air comes from natural processes that man has in various ways interfered with. The biggest sources are the bacteria inside the guts of cattle that digest grass, and other types of bacteria that thrive inside bogs and their man-made equivalent, paddy fields. The world's cattle population is growing fast and now stands at around one head of cattle for every four people. Paddy fields, which occupy 1.5 million cubic kilometres of the earth's surface, are much more efficient producers of methane than natural wetlands, especially in the tropics and especially when fed with fertilisers.

Burning vegetation also releases methane, whether the torch is applied to rainforests or dried fields or pastures. The clearing of forests also encourages the proliferation of termites, which thrive in grasslands, and generate large amounts of methane. More methane comes from waste tips. And about a fifth of the methane released into the air each year is ancient, created millions of years ago and released today as humans dig coal mines, tap natural gas fields and, suggests Ralph Cicerone of the NCAR and others, melt the tundra through global warming.

Scientists are very uncertain about how much methane comes from which sources. For instance, only in the late 1980s were instruments set up in the tropics to measure how much methane bubbles up out of paddy fields. And nobody knows how representative paddy fields are.

One of the big disputes is about the importance of termites. Like cattle, these insects have guts equipped with bacteria for breaking down cellulose. The termites give off methane as they work. Some estimates have put the contribution of termites to the world's methane production at about 5 million tonnes of the gas a year, roughly 1 per cent of the total emissions of methane from all sources. But Pat Zimmerman of the NCAR claims that it could be as much as 250 million tonnes, or 50 per cent, much of which is due to human activities.

'In a tropical forest you have maybe 20 different species of termites,' says Zimmerman. 'You have a complex food web and carbon that's stored in ways that the termites cannot get at easily. As soon as you cut down the forest, you have a lot of residual carbon lying around. You may eliminate 18 of those 20 species of termite, but the two species left have an ideal niche in which to expand.' Termites can lay 80 000 eggs a day, so they can rapidly expand their population to take advantage of extra food. 'The net result is that in the areas that have been cleared and burned, the population of termites may increase by a factor of four, five or even ten,' he says.

Part of the increase in concentration of methane in the air could be because it lasts longer. Methane normally survives about 10 years before being destroyed by oxidation by hydroxyl radicals, which are formed by the action of ultraviolet light on water vapour. Hydroxyl is the main cleansing system for the atmosphere, since it neutralises many pollutants. Levels of hydroxyl seem to be decreasing in the atmosphere, probably because of increasing demands on its services from acid pollutants such as sulphur dioxide and from carbon monoxide released in car exhausts.

Nitrous oxide is a dark horse in the greenhouse debate. Little is known about where it comes from, though we do know that it is accumulating in the atmosphere. Concentrations of nitrous oxide in the air are now 10 per cent above pre-industrial levels. The two most likely sources of the extra nitrous oxide are the burning of forests and grasslands and the action of bacteria in soils on nitrogen fertilisers. The latter has the potential to be a 'greenhouse timebomb' according to Cicerone. Nitrous oxide lasts at least a century in the air before being destroyed by ultraviolet radiation. This means that big emissions today would only show up slowly in the overall concentration of the gas in the air.

Zimmerman has studied the growing influence of gases such as methane and nitrous oxide in the greenhouse debate. 'The thing that's particularly disturbing,' he says, 'is that you can think of ways to control carbon dioxide emissions, but gases like methane seem to be tied directly to the food supply. It's very difficult for me to imagine that in the future, with population increasing, we will eat less food. It's hard to figure out a way that we can decouple increases in methane from increases in population. That's scary.'

If carbon dioxide has been the greenhouse gas of the twentieth century, and methane has the potential to fulfil the same role in the twenty-first century, nitrous oxide could be the threat that looms for the twenty-second century.

Chlorofluorocarbons (CFCs) were 'invented' in the 1930s by a chemist called Thomas Midgley, who also invented another environmental timebomb, leaded petrol. They are inert, non-toxic and extremely stable chemicals that are used as propellants in aerosols, in air conditioning systems and refrigerators, as solvents in the computer chip business and as a 'blowing agent' in making foam for everything from furniture to hamburger cartons. CFCs have a life expectancy in the air of around a century, and several of them have been revealed recently as the prime cause of the thinning of the ozone layer. But they are also potent greenhouse gases, responsible for up to a fifth of the enhanced greenhouse effect today. Because they survive so long in the air, their concentration will inevitably rise dramatically before falling in a few decades under the impact of the draconian measures now being take to stave off the destruction of the ozone layer.

It is often assumed that banning the CFCs that damage the ozone layer will also halt their greenhouse effect. But this is not necessarily so. Chemical companies such as DuPont in the USA and ICI in Britain intend to replace the CFCs that damage the ozone layer with other CFCs and related chemicals. Many of these are ozone-friendly but are almost as damaging as the chemicals that they are to replace. In the rush to save the ozone layer the world may be doing itself a disservice by allowing some of these chemicals to come on to the market.

Sir Crispin Tickell is Britain's ambassador to the United Nations and in 1977 he published a book, *Climatic Change and World Affairs*. He tries to take an Olympian view of the potential consequences of greenhouse warming, while being deeply

Waste dumps are an unexpected new source of methane, which is helping to warm the planet.

Clouds cool the planet by reflecting sunlight back into space.

involved in discussions at the UN about how the world should respond. 'None of us knows how far the greenhouse effect will go without some really dangerous effects developing,' he says. 'Some people believe that as the world warms up, so positive feedback will take place and it will get hotter still. Others believe that you reach a certain point at which there might be a triggering mechanism which would cause cooling to take place.'

This idea—that there may be a kind of planetary thermostat developed by natural ecosystems to cope with past disruptions to life such as the increasing heat of the sun—is highly controversial. And even those who believe that the living planet has devised such a sophisticated life-support system doubt that it could operate at the speed necessary to help us out of our current predicament.

The existence of a thermostat remains an open question, says Tickell. But 'what is not in question is that the greenhouse effect is real, that there are more and more greenhouse gases in the air and that global warming is a reasonable expectation for the immediate future. The world should be very worried about the increase in the greenhouse gases and governments now need to think very seriously about it.'

The 'most chilling' aspect of the changes ahead, says Tickell, 'is the rate of change. The world's climate has changed before. But the key point for us is that what previously took hundreds or thousands of years is now taking place in tens of years. In the past, animals and plants could adapt at a reasonable rate to changing climate. After the last ice age, for example, you get the forests moving northwards as the ice receded, the animals moved north, the fish moved north.' The natural processes of regeneration inside a forest worked sufficiently quickly to allow the forests of North America and Siberia to advance to keep pace with the changing climate. Trees died along the southern edge of the forest as they became too warm or dry, and they grew along the northern edge as the tundra receded. In North America spruce trees advanced from the central USA to southern Canada. The northern front of these forests moved 1000 kilometres, but over a period of up to 10 000 years, a rate of 10 kilometres per century. But in the next few decades, warming will happen at least ten times faster than at the end of the last ice age. New trees will not be able to grow in new territories in the north at anything like the rate that they will succumb to the heat of the south. The effect of this on ecosystems will be extremely serious. The mammoth could not survive the warming at the end of the last ice age. What price the polar bear today?

The inability of forests to expand fast enough to keep pace with climatic change is potentially extremely important for the planet as a whole because forests significantly determine the carbon content of the atmosphere. Trees suck up carbon dioxide as they grow and release it when they die. They also consume it during daytime, when they carry out photosynthesis, and give it up at night, when they 'respire'. In summer, photosynthesis outpaces respiration and in winter respiration dominates. So, since most of the world's trees are in the northern hemisphere, there is a marked annual cycle of carbon dioxide in the atmosphere, with a peak in summer and a low in late winter. The biggest respiration occurs when forests die.

96

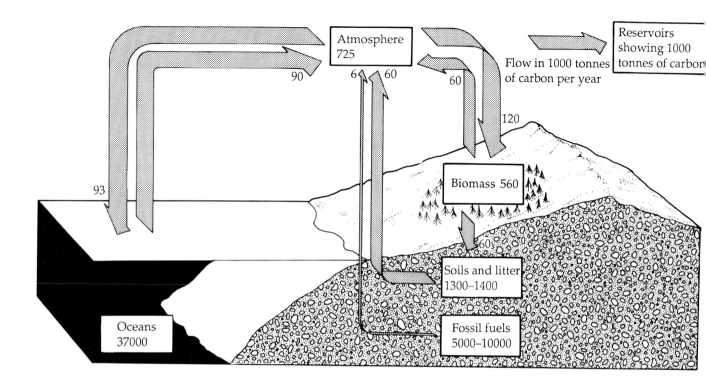

Any widespread destruction of forests due to the speed of future warming could dump masses of carbon dioxide into the atmosphere. This would be the sort of feedback that would accelerate the warming further.

CHAPTER 2

Computing the greenhouse age

The 'greenhouse effect' is a nice phrase, but not a very exact analogy with what happens in the atmosphere as we pump in more 'greenhouse gases'. A greenhouse, after all, has a physical barrier, panes of glass that keep in the sun's heat. In the atmosphere, the greenhouse effect works by affecting the balance between the radiation coming into the atmosphere from the sun and leaving again. It operates as a heat trap. The incoming shortwave radiation warms the lower layers of the atmosphere and the ground, which then radiate heat at much longer wavelengths. Much of this longwave radiation eventually escapes into space. There is a balance between the energy arriving from space and the energy leaving.

Greenhouse gases such as carbon dioxide and methane absorb some of the long-wave radiation. In so doing, they influence the temperature of the atmosphere at which incoming and outgoing energy is in balance. More greenhouse gases in the air will raise this 'equilibrium temperature'. Because the concentrations of greenhouse gases are rising today, temperatures are rising too, and will continue to rise until a new balance is struck.

If the atmosphere and land masses alone were involved, a new equilibrium temperature would be reached quickly. But most of the sun's heat strikes the oceans, which cover more than two-thirds of the planet. The oceans can transport heat to great depths as the waters slowly mix in the deep oceans, and so warm only slowly. The 'thermal inertia' of the oceans will also slow down global warming of the atmosphere and delay the greenhouse effect by perhaps 40 or 50 years. This could be helpful in giving the world time to come to terms with the warming. But it also means that there is a lot of warming 'in the pipeline' that we are already committed to receiving.

1988 saw the biggest increase ever recorded in the amount of carbon dioxide in the atmosphere. The annual average concentration exceeded 350 ppm for the first time. How far will it go? The answer is that it could go a long way. Tom Wigley says: 'If we chopped down all the world's forests and released all the carbon that is in their soils, then that alone would more than double the amount of carbon dioxide in the atmosphere. If we burnt all the fairly accessible fossil fuels—the ones that are said to be economically extractable—then we would probably multiply the amount of carbon dioxide in the atmosphere by a factor of three or four. So there is a potential to cause a really, really massive greenhouse effect ... the world could warm by as much as 8° or 9°C.'

Computer models used to predict the climate in a greenhouse world are programmed to find out what will happen if the amount of carbon dioxide and other greenhouse gases in the air double. The models predict an average warming, after the thermal inertia of the oceans is overcome, of 4°C. This warming will be greatest in winter and much greater over the polar regions. This is partly because, as ice melts, the ocean will absorb more heat, so increasing the local warming. (This 'positive feedback' is an important reason, as we saw earlier, for the planet's switching into and out of ice ages.) Another reason for intense warming at the poles is that the lower atmosphere is shallow there, so the extra warmth will be concentrated close to the Earth's surface. Temperatures are likely to rise by 8° or 9°C over the poles, which is bad news for polar bears.

The computer models of climate are still very crude. They take no account of many other 'feedbacks' that could either accelerate or reduce the warming. During 1989, scientists from round the world were working hard to refine the models and improve their forecasts in time for a World Climate Conference set for 1990. The work was being co-ordinated by Britain's Meteorological Office, which runs one of the world's premier climatic models. The hope is that the scientists can reach a consensus about the likely consequences of the greenhouse effect over the next 50 years, and offer some proposals for action by governments.

The pressure for scientists to produce results is intense. Several of the world's leading modellers say that they fear conflict with the politicians, who insist on being given firm predictions before taking action to curb global warming. Nicholas Ridley, Britain's then environment secretary, was a case in point. He said in mid-1989 that it would probably be a 'very very long time' before the science is good enough. The scientists say that by the time they are certain about their fears it will be too late to stop them becoming reality.

How good is the current generation of models? Critics warn that if you put garbage into them you will get garbage out. They mean that the data about the state of our planet and how the atmosphere works are not sufficiently good for the models, however sophisticated, to produce reliable predictions. Reid Bryson does not believe that the predicted warming will occur, for instance. 'A model is nothing but a mathematical statement of what your theory is of how things work,' he says. And he does not believe the theory. Wally Broecker from Columbia University fears events much worse than those suggested by the models, such as a lurch in ocean circulation that could turn our climate upside down. He says that 'the models that we have now are very conservative. They don't allow outrageous things to happen. The things I'm talking about cannot possibly happen in the models because they're not programmed into the models.' Others are uneasy that all the major models agree so much.

Stephen Schneider, from the National Center for Atmospheric Research in the USA, is one of the top model-makers. He accepts their failings. 'A lot of people ask why we should make trillion-dollar decisions about the future based upon computer models, models that we who make them admit have lots of uncertainties. It's a very good question. The problem is that if you absolutely have to prove all possible threats beyond a reasonable doubt, then there's really only one way to do it, and that's to perform the experiment on the one laboratory we've got—the Earth, with us and all the living things.

'The key is to find a way to validate our models. The first thing to do is to ask how well the models reproduce the extremely different climates on the present Earth. Do they make the deserts hot and dry? Do they make the poles frozen? The answer is that they do. They are capturing the gross features of the Earth's climate pretty well.

'I remember once saying at a Congressional hearing that our models are able to reproduce the 15° temperature difference between winter and summer in the northern hemisphere and the 5° difference in the southern hemisphere (it's smaller by the way because of the stronger oceanic influence). One of the Congressmen said, "You mean to tell me that you guys are spending a billion dollars of our money telling us that the winter is cold and the summer is hot?" And I said: "Yes, sir, and we're very proud of it. Experiments like looking at the seasons and at ancient climates are important ways of validating our models. We go into our models and build ice caps and freeze oceans and find out that the models distribute the winds about the right way and make the monsoon belts wetter or drier at about the right time." '

The models are also able to predict correctly climatic conditions on Mars and Venus. 'That does not tell us that we have the skill to tell whether it's going to be drier in Iowa and wetter in England and that there will be floods in Bangladesh in 2020,' admits Schneider. 'But we do have the skill to say that we're moving towards unprecedentedly rapid change in the climate.'

Clouds on the horizon

Clouds, says Wigley, 'are one of the biggest areas of uncertainty in climate modelling. They are very small features and yet they have a major effect on the atmosphere.' Clouds in the lower atmosphere act as sunshades for the planet, reflecting the sun's heat back into space. But clouds such as cirrus clouds that form in the stratosphere keep us warm by reflecting back down heat that is radiated from the Earth. If greenhouse warming produces more clouds in the lower atmosphere (which it might if the predictions that a warmer world will also be a wetter world are true), then this cloud will help keep temperatures down, providing a 'negative feedback'.

In current models, says Wigley, 'clouds are very crudely approximated. We know from satellite measurements that year-to-year changes in cloudiness and month-to-month changes are very substantial and they have a big effect on the Earth's radiation balance. So it's really important to predict how clouds might

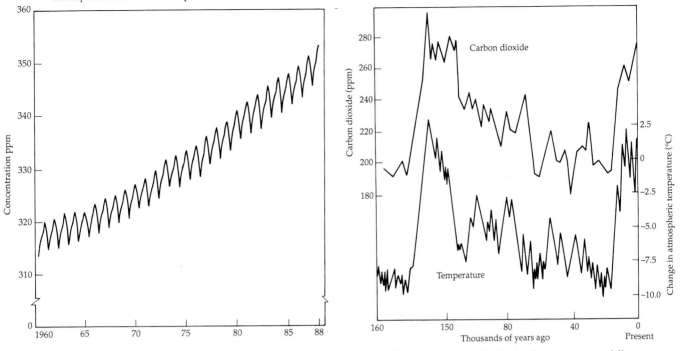

Historically where carbon dioxide leads, temperature follows.

change. People believe that there is a major deficiency in the way that clouds are modelled. Because of this, we might be overestimating the magnitude of the greenhouse effect.'

Another possible negative feedback, which could shut down global warming, is called the 'carbon dioxide fertilisation effect'. Horticulturalists know that if they inject extra carbon dioxide into a glass greenhouse they can produce bigger and faster-growing plants. This is because the process of photosynthesis, which converts carbon dioxide into plant matter, speeds up. Faster photosynthesis uses up more carbon dioxide and, if it happened on a global scale, would reduce the amount of carbon dioxide in the atmosphere. Some researchers believe that carbon dioxide fertilisation could go a long way to extinguishing greenhouse warming. They point towards studies that show trees growing faster in the increasing levels of carbon dioxide already seen in the modern world. But Richard Warrick of the Climatic Research Unit says that 'in general, fertilisation will have a rather small effect on the atmospheric concentration of carbon dioxide. For the most part, it will just increase turnover. We'll have more carbon going into plants but also more returning to the atmosphere. If, on the other hand, the forests were to increase in size and there was more carbon locked up for longer periods of time in forests, that might well affect atmospheric concentrations.'

Schneider takes up the point. It is conceivable, he believes, that the fertilisation effect might slow down the accumulation of carbon dioxide in the air, making the

101

doubling time 70 years, perhaps, rather than 50 years. 'But if fertilisation increases the amount of "biomass" in forests, it will also soon increase the amount of dead matter on the forest floors.' At any one time, there is usually around twice as much carbon tied up in forest soils as in the trees themselves. As the dead matter decays, it releases carbon dioxide back into the atmosphere. The rate at which this decomposition takes place increases with temperature. Schneider believes that 'the pulse of carbon dioxide from the decomposition of dead organic matter in the soil is likely to overwhelm the fertilisation effect, giving us a positive feedback, making things worse than we thought.' If forests die out over large areas of the world because the climate is changing too fast for them, that too would negate any carbon dioxide fertilisation effect.

Schneider's colleagues at the National Center for Atmospheric Research, Pat Zimmerman and Lee Klinger, believe that the 'positive feedback' from soils in a warmer world could be even greater in the peat bogs that blanket much of the northern latitudes of the continents, from the Hudson Bay of northern Canada to Siberia as well as parts of the tropics. These bogs store huge amounts of carbon, both as fossilised wood and as methane, much of which is trapped in the frozen bogs known as the tundra. Zimmerman and Klinger believe that processes in the bogs of the tropics could have played an important role in starting and ending the ice ages.

Trees that fall into bogs escape the normal processes of decay because the bogs contain no oxygen, which is essential to decay and to the eventual release of carbon dioxide back into the atmosphere. Over tens of millions of years, the trees are converted into coal and oil, the fossil fuels that we are burning in such quantities today. But nature too may have ways of releasing this fossilised carbon. 'We're trying to explore the links between how carbon gets stored in different areas of the world and how and when that carbon gets reconverted back into gases,' says Zimmerman. 'It is very difficult to store carbon. If you grow a tree, you've only stored the carbon for maybe 100 years or so. When the tree dies the carbon ends up back in the atmosphere. One way that you can store carbon over long periods is in peat bogs.'

Zimmerman imagines a time when the Earth is cooling and rather wet, perhaps at the start of an ice age. Much of the world will be boggy and moss will form. 'The mosses produce acid and the acid kills trees. The bogs then accumulate carbon and you end up with big pools of carbon.' Methane tied up in bogs means that there is less in the atmosphere, and in this way the bogs help to cool the planet. As the ice age intensifies, a lot of the world's moisture becomes tied up in the growing ice caps at the poles and the tropics gradually become drier. 'At the end of the ice age when the peat bogs of the tropics have dried out, termites move in and eat the accumulated carbon, converting it back into methane and carbon dioxide.' That would accelerate the ending of the ice age since termites liberate carbon from fossilised carbon just as assuredly as our own power stations and internal combustion engines do today by burning coal and oil.

The theory is a nice collision of two enthusiasms. Klinger is by his own admission a 'bogs freak', while Zimmerman has pioneered studies of the role of the termite in the planet's history. It is all very speculative, agrees Zimmerman, but it fits recent data culled from ice cores about the fall and rise of methane levels in the atmosphere as the world switches into and out of ice ages. Whatever the truth, research into such ideas is essential if we are to avoid being hijacked by some lethal surprise in the fast-changing greenhouse world.

Methane could well turn out to be the joker in the greenhouse pack. There is growing interest in the idea that some greenhouse Doomsday Machine could be at work in the icy tundras of the north or, perhaps, in the sediments beneath the oceans. The tundras contain large amounts of fossil methane, trapped where it was produced in the bogs before they froze. One recent estimate is that about 14 per cent of the Earth's organic carbon is tied up in the tundras. As the world warms, the tundras will melt and the methane could be released, creating a strong positive feedback for global warming. There is also fossilised methane held under pressure at the bottom of the oceans in lattice-like structures called clathrates. This too, could be released by global warming or changing sea levels.

Another more heretical notion comes from Reid Bryson. He is a dust freak. 'I got interested in the question of dust in the atmosphere back during the Second World War when I was stationed in Puerto Rico. About five days after every big tank battle on the other side of the Atlantic in North Africa, we would see a cloud of dust coming over at 10 000–20 000 feet. Our weather balloons would disappear into the dust. Later I went to India, probably the dustiest place in the world in springtime, and measured the amount of dust in the air and its effect on radiation.' Bryson's complaint is that current climate models ignore dust. 'If the model assumes that there is nothing in the atmosphere but pure gas, that isn't very realistic,' he says. The models that predict global warming assume that carbon dioxide will warm the planet by absorbing heat at certain wavelengths. But Bryson believes that dust is already absorbing much of the heat radiated from the surface of the Earth at these wavelengths. This overlap between carbon dioxide and dust ensures, he says, that any increase in carbon dioxide will not have such an important effect. 'Most radiation models,' he says, 'do not take that overlap between dust and carbon dioxide into account.'

Dust, like clouds, is a double-edged weapon in the greenhouse argument, however. Depending on characteristics and where it is, dust can both heat or cool the earth. One of the most important sources of dust in the atmosphere is volcanic eruption, which prevents the sun's heat from reaching the Earth's surface.

The balance between the two roles is obviously crucial. There are other confusions. During the most recent ice age the world was a much dustier place. One estimate is that there was ten times as much dust in the atmosphere then, at a time when carbon dioxide levels in the air were much lower. That fact strongly suggests, say Bryson's critics, that carbon dioxide is a more important element in the greenhouse than dust.

Floods around the North Sea killed many hundreds of people during the storms of 1953. Holland suffered worst (left). Soon, many of the world's great cities, such as Venice (above), could be submerged.

CHAPTER 3

Waking the giant

The oceans are the sleeping giants of the greenhouse debate. They are the biggest unknown, the least well modelled part of the equation. And yet in every sense they can swamp what happens elsewhere on the planet. The oceans, for instance, contain some 60 times more carbon than the atmosphere and there is a regular large-scale exchange of carbon between the oceans and the air. People are shocked that half of all the carbon dioxide emitted into the atmosphere since the start of the industrial revolution is still there. But it is even more remarkable that the other half has been absorbed by the oceans. One of the questions for the future is whether the oceans can continue with this helpful disappearing act as we pump ever more carbon dioxide into the atmosphere. Many scientists believe that the oceans could be close to calling a halt to their beneficence.

Life in the oceans is essential to their ability to absorb carbon dioxide from the air at anything like its current rate. The process is often called the 'biological pump' because of the efficiency with which carbon is pumped from the atmosphere to the ocean depths. The pump works because to construct their bodies, organisms, especially plankton, in the surface waters of the ocean absorb carbon dioxide dissolved in the water. The gas is swiftly replaced with new carbon dioxide from the atmosphere. The organisms can then drop carbon towards the ocean floor either in their skeletons when they die or in their faeces. The carbon may be dissolved in water and reconsumed by other organisms many times on its way down, but eventually it reaches the bottom where, over the aeons, it will form layers of limestone rock that may one day help form new continents. Without the biological pump, there would be much more carbon dioxide in the air and the world would be a much hotter place.

As well as absorbing carbon dioxide, the oceans have also taken up much of the extra heat that the greenhouse gases trap in the air. But again the question remains whether they will be able to maintain this role. Wally Broecker's evidence of the activity of the oceans at the beginning and end of the ice ages suggests that we could be dealing with a hair-trigger mechanism which may have some nasty shocks in store for us.

As well as having a big say in the global heat and carbon balances of our planet, the oceans also strongly influence regional climates. They do this partly by distributing heat around the planet, a duty which they divide about half and half

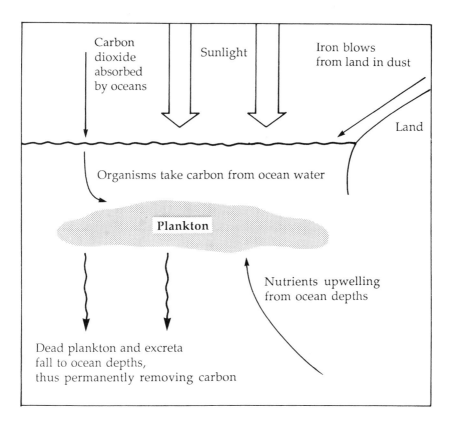

The 'biological pump'. In most places the supply of nutrients and iron limits the growth of plankton, such as the picturesque shown below – and hence the ability of marine organisms to absorb carbon dioxide from the air.

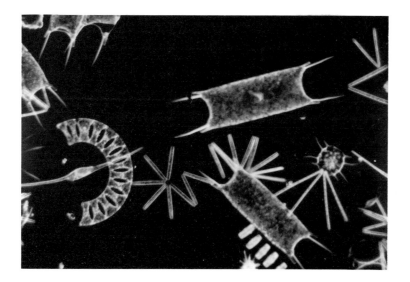

with the atmosphere. Each day the Gulf Stream in the Atlantic Ocean transports northwards from the equator an amount of heat equal to the output of a million nuclear power stations. This heat is then taken up by westerly winds that keep Europe warm. Without the Gulf Stream Europe would be a very much cooler place. The Gulf Stream is also part of a fundamental feature of the oceans called the 'deep ocean circulatory system', which transports heat, carbon and other elements to the deep ocean, which is otherwise largely cut off from the surface layers. The cooled remains of the Gulf Stream plunge to the ocean depths in the far northern Atlantic Ocean and spend around a thousand years at the ocean bottom before surfacing again.

Anything that wakes the sleeping giant, that upsets the ocean's mixing processes or breaks the biological pump, could upset the planet. That is Wally Broecker's fear when he talks of the deep ocean circulation blowing a fuse, as it apparently did during the last ice age. Tom Wigley fears the same thing. 'The whole system could change to a situation where, for example, there was a lot more deep water formation or maybe no deep water formation. That would have a feedback effect on the climate system, a very rapid change caused by the ocean circulation.' As Broecker points out, the current climate models do not even allow for the possibility of such an effect.

While the scientists attempt to come to grips with their models, most people's concerns about the oceans and the greenhouse effect centre on the fear of rising sea levels. The oceans have been rising for around a century now, at a rate of 1–2 millimetres a year, probably as a result of a phenomenon known as 'thermal expansion' whereby objects expand as they become warmer. With the oceans up to 5 kilometres deep in many places, a tiny expansion will flood out people living on flat shorelines or the coral islands of the Pacific, few of which reach more than 2 metres above the current sea level.

Toodle-oo Tuvalu

Tuvalu is the smallest nation on earth. The former Ellice Islands, it gained independence from Britain a decade ago but may never see its first centenary. Its 8000 inhabitants may be ferried to a new home long before the waves finally engulf the string of coral islands. After all, who will want to invest in building factories or schools or hospitals in a country doomed to disappear beneath rising tides? The Prime Minister of Tuvalu, Dr Tomasi Puapua, in drawing attention to his country's crisis, does not add to confidence about its future. He said in 1988: 'There is nothing we can do. Maybe all of us will have to go to Australia. I am very worried. My people, well, they are not so worried because they are very religious and they believe in the Almighty. But I trained as a doctor. That's scientific and you know I am very worried indeed.'

Tuvalu came close to obliteration in 1972 when five people died as a spring tide, topped by 50-foot waves whipped up by a typhoon which washed across most of the islands. The homes of Tuvaluans are built on stilts, but even so almost any rise in sea levels would leave the nation impossibly vulnerable to the next serious storm.

Tuvalu would be very expensive to defend against the sea. The main atoll, called Funafuti, is so narrow that to protect its 2.5 square kilometres, engineers would have to build 54 kilometres of sea walls, according to a study for the Commonwealth Secretariat. Moreover, because the coral that makes up the island is porous and sea water can invade it, the land within the sea walls would have to be raised or else it would be flooded from within as sea levels rise. Such 'citadels of the sea' are an unlikely proposition concluded the author of the study of Tuvalu, James Lewis from Bath University.

There is a precedent, however. Japan has plans to spend $240 million to raise by about three metres the level of a tiny islet the size of a table called Okinotorishima that it owns in the Pacific. The purpose is to save not so much the island as the 360 000 square kilometres of ocean, rich in fish and minerals, that Japan claims because of its title to the island.

Tuvalu's neighbour 1000 kilometres across the South Pacific is Kiribati (population 64 000). It too faces a bleak future, as do the Maldives in the Indian Ocean, a nation of 1200 coral islands which seems set for a prosperous future as a holiday centre offering breathtaking trips to coral reefs. But rising seas could kill the coral even before it inundates the islands. The Maldives had an early taste of things to come in 1987 when a storm brought record floods during which inhabitants speared fish in the streets. A Dutch quango called Delft Hydraulics has conducted a study of the island's problems. Peter Shröder says that the main finding was that the islanders are in effect destroying the island's natural defences. The islands are flat sand pancakes on top of coral reefs. 'The coral reefs form a natural protection against the waves.' But coral is the islanders' only building material. If sea defences have to be raised 'they take coral to build little dykes to protect themselves. This is just going round in circles', says Shroder.' For houses, dykes and reservoirs, the islanders currently use around 1 million cubic metres of coral each year, slowly eating away their islands as the seas rise.

Tuvalu, Kiribati and the Maldives, along with the Marshall Islands and the Line Islands (both under the protection of the USA) and Tokelau, which is controlled by New Zealand, are listed by the UN's Environment Programme as places which 'will become uninhabitable by the middle of the next century if predicted sea level rises occur'.

In early 1989, a British environmental group called Ark published maps showing the devastating effect of a 5 metre rise in sea levels for Britain. And it handed out mock postcards from 'Blackpool: The Sunshine Isle! Frequent ferries from Preston' and posters for racing at Doncaster—sea horse racing, that is. All this could happen, Ark suggested, within 70 years. Such large rises in sea levels were considered possible by some scientists a few years ago because of fears that

Ark's postcard for the future.

the ice caps of Antarctica and Greenland could melt swiftly. But today no scientist of repute believes that anything so extreme is probable. Even fellow environmental campaigners such as Charles Secrett of Friends of the Earth pour scorn on Ark's prediction, calling it wild and inaccurate. 'It doesn't help anyone to make statements like that,' he said.

There is, none the less, growing uncertainty about how great the rise in sea levels will be. Few doubt that the rises of recent decades, due to thermal expansion, will continue at an increasing rate. But fears that ice caps could begin to melt are increasingly questioned. New climate models instead suggest that increased rainfall will lead to more snow falling in the polar regions. So the ice caps could grow rather than melt away—at least for a few decades. There remains, however, a third possibility which could make all Ark's most dire warnings come true. This is that the extra load of snow on the ice caps could make them mechanically unstable. If the caps then start to move, like a vast icy version of Aberfan's slag heap, they

110

would soon push thousands of icebergs into the oceans. As the icebergs melt they could raise sea levels by several metres. The West Antarctic ice sheet is the most likely to go. It is precariously attached to an underwater archipelago and held in place by sheets of ice that are, in the words of one researcher, 'like the cork in a champagne bottle'. A small rise in the temperature of ocean currents that flow round and under these sheets could unleash a catastrophic break-up of the whole West Antarctic ice sheet. That would raise sea levels by about 6 metres.

Assuming this does not happen, scientists at the Climatic Research Unit now put the likely rise in sea levels at perhaps 50 centimetres over the next 50 years. The danger is that by comparison with higher figures, such numbers sound reassuring. But they remain a huge threat to the future of many countries. About half of the world's population lives in cities or farmland close to the sea and hundreds of millions of people might be vulnerable. Half of Bangladesh's 100 million people, for instance, live on the delta of the River Ganges and might be permanently flooded out of their homes. Even if the delta were not to be flooded permanently, the encroaching sea could swiftly contaminate the soil with salt so that crops would not grow.

The millions of people living on the Nile delta in Egypt are in a similar position, and the city of Alexandria is specially threatened. The seas might also inundate great cities from Bangkok to Venice and from New York to Sydney. Indonesia, a vast collection of islands in the Far East, has 15 per cent of the world's coastline, and at least 40 per cent of its land surface is vulnerable to rising sea levels. The government is moving millions of people from overpopulated Java to the tidal swamps of Sumatra and Borneo, where they are likely to be greeted by rising tides.

Disasters will come to coastal communities in two forms: permanent inundation of land, forcing people to move; and sudden death, when storms breach sea walls made feeble by rising sea levels. The disaster that hit East Anglia and the Thames estuary in 1953 is now a fading memory. A storm surge from the North Sea took 350 lives in England and a further 1600 in the Netherlands. The £300 million Thames Barrier was built to prevent a future tidal surge inundating central London. But it may soon be inadequate and killer floods may return.

Besides flooding low-lying land, the seas will eat away at exposed cliffs with new vigour. John Brown knows what it feels like. He lives on a clifftop at Fairlight in Sussex, a village of 50 homes that will disappear into the sea when the cliffs crumble. 'We're about 90 feet high here,' he says. But that will not save his garden. He has already lost 30 feet and there is 60 feet left between the cliff and his house. Soon many people will be in his position. 'The effect of a rising tide will be terrible, it really will,' he says. 'People will feel shock and fear. They will feel as they did under the bombs during the war—nothing they could do about it.' The cost of saving this one tiny village is put by engineers at £3.5 million.

Floods have a history of taking human life. Hubert Lamb has researched storms in the North Sea. He found that 'between AD 1099 and 1570, at least 286 towns, villages and parishes and many islands were lost in 30 floods. On Christmas Day,

1717, 12 000 lives were lost mainly in Emden on the German coast.' One flood in 1212 some drowned 300 000 people in northern Holland.

Modern sea defences and improved weather forecasting have saved most countries from this kind of death toll. But Bangladesh, where around 700 000 people died when a cyclone caused a tidal surge in the Bay of Bengal in 1970, remains vulnerable. Unless nations respond to the threat of rising sea levels, even the rich world may see disasters on this scale again.

In the Netherlands they are used to dealing with threats from the sea. They have in recent years battled to reclaim most of the IJsselmeer Zuider Zee, which was inundated by the North Sea at the height of the little ice age. Shröder of Delft Hydraulics says: 'We think we can just about manage. We have to build higher dykes, but we are contemplating extreme solutions. The real worry for us is that the rise in sea levels will cause salt to get into groundwaters and poison our fields. Plans exist for flooding part of the country again with the water from the Rhine to make sure that the water table has fresh water.' Salt water already penetrates some 50 kilometres upstream of the mouth of the River Rhine, according to Gjerrit Hekstra of the Dutch environment ministry. He puts the cost of rebuilding Dutch sea defences to cope with a rise in sea levels of 1 metre at $3 billion, with a similar sum for bolstering defences inland. Few poor countries will be able to contemplate such expenditure for their own coasts.

Hekstra, writing in *The Ecologist* journal, says that something like 5 million square kilometres of land around the world are threatened by a rise in sea levels of 1 metre. This is roughly 3 per cent of the land area of the globe, but one-third of the total cropland of the world. 'Much of the threatened land is densely populated and includes many large cities; indeed, as many as one billion people may be at risk,' he says. London, New York, Miami, Bangkok, Venice, Sydney—all are very vulnerable to inundation.

The American drought of 1988 brought fears that the coming Greenhouse Age may produce permanent dust bowl conditions in the grain fields of the Midwest.

CHAPTER 4

The global greenhouse

Two events in 1988 increased concern that our climate is showing signs of the greenhouse in action. One was the drought in the American Midwest. In June 1988 pictures of parched grain fields jostled in the world's press with stories that the 'old man' Mississippi had suddenly stopped rollin'. Then a top American climate modeller, James Hansen from NASA, told a Congressional committee that it was all probably due to the greenhouse effect. This assertion was based on a scientific paper that he was about to publish, which predicted many more droughts in the midwest during the 1990s as the greenhouse effect got going.

Many climatologists thought he was talking nonsense. Their papers, published in early 1989, suggested that the real culprit in the drought was the ocean current known as 'La Niña', which was then rolling fiercely across the Pacific Ocean. Ironically, 'La Niña' was cooling the ocean and subsequently the atmosphere for a time. This does not prove anybody wrong. The greenhouse could well be an underlying cause of the drought. But it does show that the world likes a simple story and that climate is a complicated business.

Climatologists took rather more notice, as a sign of a changing world, of Hurricane Gilbert, which swept through the Caribbean in the autumn of 1988. It too appeared to be an embodiment of one of the predictions of the climate models: that tropical storms will become much more intense as the oceans warm. These storms derive their strength from the heat of the oceans and the massive amounts of energy generated when water vapour condenses to form droplets in a cloud. Hurricane Gilbert was the worst tropical storm in the Caribbean for a century and came during the hottest year for a century. But that too could be just a coincidence.

The present generation of climatic models is a little shaky about predicting global changes and rough and ready in the extreme when it comes to pinpointing regional consequences of global warming. Some models, for instance, do not predict the kind of American droughts that Hansen believes will occur. The model run by the Met Office in Britain suggests that the Midwest will become wetter. Similarly, some models predict drier times for the Sahel, while others say that its rains will return before long. Since there is also so much variability in the climatic system, it is little more than a stab in the dark to claim that a particular event is caused by the greenhouse effect.

The world cannot wait for perfection in the models, however. And some scientists are willing to stick their necks out with some predictions, though they prefer the word 'scenarios'. Mick Kelly at the Climatic Research Unit is bolder than most in his potted version of the future:

'There are three general areas in which we can be pretty certain about impacts. First of all, the temperature change will be greatest at the poles, particularly in winter, and this will have a major effect on the sea ice, on local ecosystems and the lives of the native inhabitants. The second major area of impact is in middle latitudes; there we may see the drying out of continental interiors—of North America, of Europe and also central Asia. Finally at lower latitudes, it is likely that the drier regions will become drier; many of the wetter regions will become wetter. There may be a major shift in the character of the monsoon. It will become more intense in the southern part of the region, but less intense in the north—it won't penetrate as far northwards. And this will have major consequences for water supply.'

The Asian monsoon, says Kelly, is a good example of how regional climates will be changed by global warming and of the difficulties of guessing what will happen. 'The monsoon is essentially a large sea breeze. As the Asian continent warms up during the summer, hot air over the continental land mass rises and draws in air from the cooler ocean. And that brings moisture. As the moisture-laden air rises over the continent, the rain falls. That is basically the monsoon.' In future, the spring warming of the continent is likely to occur earlier. That will mean an earlier onset of the monsoon circulation. That we can say for sure. What we are not too certain about is what the net effect will be on the amount of water falling over different parts of India during the course of the monsoon season.'

Many researchers believe that India may become much wetter than it is today. Rivers such as the Indus, Irrawaddy and Ganges may overflow, but they may also provide plenty of water for bumper rice crops. On the other hand, dry areas such as the desert of Rajasthan in northwest India could spread.

The impact of warming on 'El Niño' could be even more important. 'There's a very strong link between global warming and the 'El Niño' phenomenon,' says Kelly. 'As the temperature of the Pacific rises during the course of an 'El Niño' event, there's a detectable effect on global temperature. Equally, as temperatures rise worldwide, it is likely that there will be more warming of the equatorial Pacific, and that could result in more intense 'El Niños'. This is a process that is too sophisticated for our models to predict with any certainty at the moment. But it may be no coincidence that the most intense 'El Niño' event this century occurred early during the 1980s, at a time when the global temperature was reaching a record high.' Hansen believes that global warming will be at its most intense in the coming decades in the tropical Pacific, where 'El Niño' originates.

Will there be any winners as the world's climatic pack is shuffled? Some say that the Soviet Union could do well. Siberia could suddenly be offered all-year-round ports along its Arctic coast, which will have profound military consequences. And Siberia's climate could become fit for growing grain provided that its soils are adequate. But any gain for Siberia might be more than counterbalanced by a drying out of the country's current grain-producing area, the Ukraine.

Alan Robock has been active in a scientific exchange programme between the USA and the Soviet Union. For the past 15 years, scientists have been looking at climatic change. 'I first had the opportunity to go to the Soviet Union 10 years ago for a meeting on climate and that was when we recognised that greenhouse warming might be a problem,' he says. 'But the rest of the world wasn't nearly so concerned about it. I've done research with data I've collected from the Soviet Union. As they don't have the same computer capabilities that we have, they've been able to come to our country to do more sophisticated calculations. But they've produced a lot of interesting theories that lead the way in other areas.'

Robock says that there is still uncertainty in the USSR about how they will fare in a greenhouse world. 'There is one Russian scientist, Mikhail Budyko, who is one of the most famous climatologists in the world and did pioneering work on climate modelling. He first warned us about the greenhouse effect. I understand that he thinks that perhaps the Soviet Union might gain.'

Budyko himself goes further than this. He believes that on balance the world can gain from the greenhouse effect. He finds himself in an odd position, he says. After being the first person to warn that global warming may happen, he was cast as a radical. But he now appears, he says as 'a conservative' not unhappy with a warmer future, while all around him predict catastrophe. 'At the very beginning of discussion of this problem, I think I was in a minority of one,' he says, 'because for some time, probably a few years, nobody believed in such a possibility.'

At the heart of Budyko's optimism lies a belief that the world's tropical deserts will not, as most experts predict, expand, engulfing farmland. Instead, he says, the deserts will contract in the coming decades. This idea comes from a completely different approach from that adopted by his western colleagues. While westerners have built ever more powerful computer models, Budyko, who lacks computer facilities in his own country, has built on the long national scientific tradition of palaeoclimatology. The most recent such period when the world was warmer than today was some 6000 years ago, when global temperatures were about 1° warmer. Before that, between the last two ice ages around 130 000 years ago, temperatures were perhaps 2° warmer.

Predictions about future climate based on palaeoclimatology offer some similarities with computer models. The higher temperatures were most marked in winter and at high latitudes, for instance. But Budyko's ideas about rainfall, which the modellers acknowledge are only crudely predicted by the computers, diverge wildly from the models. His studies show that 'in warm epochs there was no desert in the globe'. The Sahara and the deserts of the Middle East were wet and lush enough to form the environment in which the first civilisations could flourish. Going back 10 million years to before the era of the ice ages, 'almost all the continent of Africa was covered by wet tropical forest' in which the apes ruled. The decline of the forests, as we have seen, caused apes to evolve in ways that allowed

116

them to hunt and survive on the grasslands—and hence to become human. But it also made life harder. Budyko sees the return of a warmer, wetter world as in some ways 'Paradise regained'.

Budyko believes that a warming of the planet by humans will have the same effect of increasing rainfall as past natural warmings. In the coming decades, he says, 'deserts will probably be much easier to use for agriculture,' like the cold areas of the north, such as Siberia. He does concede that some areas may suffer. He predicts that rainfall will decline in the American Midwest 'by something like 2.2 centimetres per year', but 'the great majority of continents will be more moist.' He foretells a 50 per cent increase in rainfall in the dry regions of central Asia by the year 2000, increasing to a 100 per cent rise by 2050.

The test case will be Africa. While some see the desiccation of Africa in the past two decades as the first sign of the greenhouse effect taking hold, Budyko feels this is an aberration. He predicts 'enormous increases in precipitation in the Sahara— enormous, 30 centimetres. The Sahara will be a quite different place in the next 10 years or so. To believe this is difficult because 30 centimetres of precipitation is quite enough to have a considerable number of animals, to feed horses and cattle and so on.'

'There seems to be a political consensus that global change in climate is bad,' says Budyko. 'But it's quite possible that the general result of global warming will be favourable ... improving our climate.' Not surprisingly, therefore, he sees no great urgency in halting the greenhouse warming, but suggests instead that the world 'use the positive effects'.

Budyko's colleague in Moscow, Anatoli Golitsyn, takes the middle ground. The greenhouse, he says, 'might be beneficial for the Soviet Union'. But rainfall is not the only issue. In a warmer world, 'you may have more precipitation, but evaporation would be faster and the net result would be the drying of the soil.' Soil moisture is, he says, the key issue for the future of farming.

As fellow inhabitants of the northern latitudes, the Canadians, like the Russians, have reasons to hope that the greenhouse may be a blessing. Some Canadian researchers have argued that, just as the Ukraine's loss could be Siberia's gain, so the USA's loss could be the making of parts of Canada. 'It's been suggested that Canada will gain because it will get warmer there and their agriculture will improve,' says Robock. But the mid-continental drying that could decimate grain production in the US Midwest might also put Canadians in the same boat as their fellow farmers south of the border.

Martin Parry, the head of the Atmospheric Impacts Research Group at Birmingham University, has compiled a detailed study of the likely impact of global warming on the world's agriculture which was published in late 1988 by an international think tank called the International Institute for Applied Systems Analysis. Parry's scenarios (not predictions, he pleads) suggest that many of the winners could find their victories elusive.

There is likely to be a big increase in rice production in Japan, for instance, 'creating an acute surplus of expensive rice that would require drastic government action to dispose of'. Rice production in Japan is massively subsidised by the government, with domestic prices currently three or four times those on the world market. So 'the build-up of an enormous rice surplus could become an important economic issue, putting into question traditional government policies,' says the report.

Parry believes that 'the prairie wheatbelt of the USA and Canada may return to the dry and windy "dust bowl" conditions experienced in the 1930s. A study of the Canadian province of Saskatchewan suggested that thousands of jobs could be lost in the province. If the monsoons and 'El Niños' intensify, then Brazil, Australia, India and parts of Africa might find themselves on a dangerous switchback, alternating between good crops and intense drought, says Parry. But at the same time, northern countries such as Finland and Iceland could find a 'new bounty' in their fields.

What of Britain? The country has hardly noticed any local signs of the global warming that statisticians insist has taken place round the world in the past decade. In fact, says Mick Kelly, 'over the past 20 years or so, while much of the northern hemisphere has been warming up, the temperature of western Europe has remained pretty stable.' This may be due to the effect of the Atlantic Ocean. The oceans take time to warm up and it is possible that because the Atlantic to the west of us has not warmed up as yet, our temperatures have remained relatively constant.

How long will this continue? It is unlikely that the ocean effect will offset the warming for very long, says Kelly. 'There are indications that significant warming will affect the UK during the 1990s.' Within the next few decades Britain's weather may 'become more like that of southwest France, Biarritz in summer for example. In winter we may bask in the kind of weather that southern Spain gets today.

Parry painted a rosy picture of the future for farmers at a lecture in May 1989 organised by the National Farmers Union. As fields dry out in the American Midwest and the Mediterranean, northern Europe may cash in. Maize, sunflowers and soya may become important British crops. Southern England might be able to grow the nation's baked beans, which are at present rarely grown north of Italy.

Whether all this happens, he agrees, depends on rainfall. Some researchers believe that while tropical storms will be more intense in the greenhouse world, storms in the mid-latitudes, the kind that bring Britain most of its rain, may moderate. The mid-latitude rain-bearing weather systems gain their strength from the contrast between warm air moving north from the tropics and cool air moving south from the Arctic. Since the polar regions are set to warm much more than the tropics, this contrast will diminish. The rain systems that currently often queue up over the Atlantic to dump their rain on us may become weaker and are more likely to be diverted by 'blocking' zones of high pressure, known as anticyclones, which bring dry weather.

Kelly says that 'in the United Kingdom, there are indications that the amount of rainfall we receive in spring and early summer will be much reduced ... because there will be fewer depressions passing over the country and more stable anti-cyclones.' In late summer, however, the risk of thunderstorms, fuelled by hot land setting up convection currents, may increase. This shift in the distribution of rainfall with seasons may have major consequences for agriculture, says Kelly. It could be as important perhaps as the warming itself. Crops may face a dry summer, followed by torrential rains that flatten fields in the weeks before the harvest is due to be brought in. 'For many crops, an increase in temperature will result in better harvests' in Britain. 'But reduced rainfall will offset any benefits due to the rise in temperature.' Kelly's colleague, Richard Warrick, adds that warmer temperatures 'speed a plant through its development processes quicker, and if this occurs during the critical period of grain formation, then the yield is less.'

In all this there is great scope for optimism and pessimism. Wigley admits that his idea of a Spanish-style winter could prove illusory. The trouble is that feeble rain-bearing systems may give us a warmer, drier summer, but they may also allow a colder, snowier winter. The Atlantic systems vie over Britain for supremacy with cold anticyclonic air from Siberia. In future, the Siberian air may win more often. Researches by Wigley's colleagues into weather records of the past century have backed this idea. They show that when the world has been warmer, Siberian anticyclones have become more intense over Europe in winter.

Lawrence Woodham, a farmer at Battle in Sussex, took a rosy view when confronted by TV cameras. 'If we could grow avocados and that sort of thing, I'm sure we'd be quite happy,' he laughed. 'I don't think it need be bad news. Farming is a question of adaptation to the conditions, and if temperatures change we can grow new crops. In the northern latitudes in which we live, the grass will grow for about six months of the year. Now if the increased temperature meant that the grass could grow for eight or ten months, we could become more like New Zealand. The cows could go out and harvest their grass every day, as opposed to now, when we have to feed them. We spend half the year being butler and manager to the herd; they could go and do it themselves.'

CHAPTER 5

A plague on the world

One of the most devastating diseases to hit the human population was the Black Death of Europe, a plague first brought by rats from China in the mid-fourteenth century. Following its first arrival in 1347, the plague killed around a third of the population of western Europe—more than 20 million people—in less than two years. From then on, the disease continued to erupt in parts of Europe from time to time until the early eighteenth century. Its last appearance in Britain came in London in the years before the Great Fire of 1666.

The plague appears to be native to Asia, where bubonic plague was rife both before and after its excursions into Europe. Research has found that the plague's origins and capacity to spread west both seem to be rooted in climatic disruptions. The outbreak that reached Europe in 1347 originated in China in 1333, the year after one of the worst floods ever, in which the Yellow River burst its banks and drowned some 7 million people. 'There can be little doubt,' says Hubert Lamb, former director of the Climatic Research Unit at East Anglia, 'that the waters had dislocated the habitats of the wildlife as well as the human settlements, including those of the plague-carrying rodents.' Driven from their nests by the floods, the rats took their diseases among the humans who had survived the waters. Soon the plague was spreading through both China and India.

In the past, such outbreaks had remained in Asia, but this time it spread west. Andy Dobson of the University of Rochester in New York believes that previous westward incursions had been prevented by the deserts of central Asia and the Middle East. But 'it seems likely that a climatic change began during the thirteenth century, which altered the position of the deserts and surrounding grasslands in Mongolia and Persia and led to a change in the trade routes between those two countries. It also allowed a change in the distribution of the populations of small mammals that acted as hosts for the plague. Together, those changes enabled the plague to spread from India and China and to reach right across to Turkey, where it eventually boarded ship and was able to spread throughout the Mediterranean and cause perhaps one of the biggest impacts on human population known.'

Rats are still a problem in Britain today—and respond to the slightest switch of climate in their favour. Two mild winters in Britain brought a boom in the country's rat population in the late 1980s, with special problems in inner city areas such as the London Borough of Haringey. The rats, whose numbers are normally held down by cold winters, have brought with them an increased incidence of Weill's Disease, a dangerous fever.

The spread of international communications means that deserts, mountain ranges and other natural barriers are no longer quite the impediment to the spread of infectious diseases that they once were. But when they are breached, the results can be devastating. The classic example is rinderpest, a measles-like virus that afflicts cattle. 'Rinderpest was completely absent in Africa south of the Sahara,' says Dobson, 'until the end of the last century, when military activities brought the Italian army to Somalia.' The soldiers brought a few cattle, which turned out to be infected with the disease. 'Within ten years it had spread from the horn of Africa to the Cape, infecting both other domestic cattle and wild animals such as the wildebeest, buffalo and antelope. 'These species had never been exposed to rinderpest and had no immunity. In those ten years, rinderpest 'killed perhaps 80 or 90 per cent of the wild game in Africa'.

The indirect effect on humans of the rinderpest plague was also horrible. Lennart Olsson, a Swedish geographer, says that a combination of drought and the arrival of rinderpest caused 'probably the worst famine ever in Africa' during the 1890s. 'In areas of the Sudan and Ethiopia, we estimate that 100 per cent of the cattle stock died and hundreds of thousands of people probably died too.' Workineh Degefu of the Ethiopian National Meteorological Services Agency agrees. Famine stalked the whole of Ethiopia between 1888 and 1892, he says. Those years are known in Ethiopian history as 'Kifu Ken', or the harsh days. Rinderpest killed 90 per cent of the country's cattle and, besides the drought, there were also plagues of locusts, caterpillars and rats. There was cannibalism, and wild animals attacked people. About a third of the human population of Ethiopia perished.

Just as diseases of temperate lands can run riot through the tropics, so tropical diseases may spread north as the climate warms. 'It seems likely to me,' says Dobson, 'that many of the diseases that are at present restricted to the tropical areas of the world would be able to move into areas such as much of southern Europe, the central and southern United States and perhaps further into the northern parts of Europe, which will experience greater climatic changes than those areas nearer the tropics.'

One disease known to take advantage of climatic change is sleeping sickness, which afflicts humans and cattle and is carried by the tsetse fly. The disease might spread from its African home. Noel Brown director of the UN's Environment Programme asks: 'What about the tsetse fly in Arizona? I don't want to be alarmist, but the fact is that these things are likely to happen and they could create very serious problems.'

Dobson's investigations in Africa have reached some surprising conclusions of southern Africa, he believes, but elsewhere, in eastern, western and central Africa, many of its current haunts may be made uninhabitable for the fly. This may be good news for farmers: but conservationists will be horrified. The retreat of the tsetse fly 'will occur in regions which are now currently given over to game

The Black Death came to Europe after weather patterns in central Asia shifted in the fourteenth century.

Sir Crispin Tickell (left) warns of the millions of homeless 'eco-refugees'. These Ethiopians seeking a new life in the Sudan (right) may be setting a new trend.

animals,' says Dobson. Cattle farmers must avoid areas infested with the tsetse fly and many such regions are today national parks. But 'in the absence of the tsetse flies, these areas will become open for humans and their cattle, and this will lead to the loss of habitat for wild animals throughout Africa.'

Dobson says that 'on the whole I am inclined to be very pessimistic about how climatic changes are likely to affect the distribution of diseases in the world. The present situation is that many of the major pathogenic diseases of humans are restricted to the tropical areas. A change of climate which increased temperature of the northern areas could only lead to a spread of those diseases into areas where they aren't already present. The diseases could also become more virulent in their heartlands, says Dobson, leading to a further increase in the enormous amounts of mortality and debilitation the diseases cause in the areas of the world where they are present today.

The most pressing case may be malaria, the fastest growing disease in the world (with the possible exception of AIDS). Malaria's host, the mosquito, is now resistant in some degree to all the drugs that humans have developed against it. The creation of a vaccine, meanwhile, is proceeding too slowly and the prospects of it being used as a control strategy for areas where malaria is endemic seem extremely low, says Dobson.

Malaria is very responsive to climatic changes. One worrying portent of how malaria may spread in the coming decades is provided by Madagascar. 'The incidence of malaria in Madagascar has increased enormously in the past ten years,' says Dobson. 'One figure suggests as many as 100 000 new cases in the last couple of years.' One theory for this rise is that Madagascar's climate has changed, partly because of rainforest destruction.

Ecological refugees

Sir Crispin Tickell is more concerned with migrating humans. He believes that, just as the tsetse may be banished from large parts of Africa, so tens of millions of people may also find themselves on the move. Floods will be the most immediate problem. The prospects for eco-refugees and even eco-wars are considerable. 'Drastic change means that the old problems which affect human history back as far as it has been recorded will return. Shortage of water and violent change in geographical circumstances are going to cause people to move. In the past, when the world was a big place and the human population was a relatively sparse species, there was always a simple answer to climate change: people got up and walked somewhere else. At the end of the last ice age, 10 000 years ago, you have a movement of human populations, like the movement of animals and trees, northwards in the northern hemisphere, southwards in the southern hemisphere. Now you have the same prospect, but in a very short space of time and in a heavily populated planet. There will be major difficulties because as you get a wave of refugees coming up from somewhere, there will be a man at the border asking for their passports. You can imagine very big problems beginning.'

One example might be millions of Bangladeshis, their homes flooded for good, queuing up at the border with India, asking to be allowed to live in Bengal. What happens if the Indians say no?

Droughts in Africa have provided a microcosm of what may happen in the coming century, says Tickell. 'There are Ethiopian refugees all over the world, but in particular in neighbouring Sudan. There are also Sudanese refugees moving in different directions, some into Ethiopia. And there are Somali refugees in Ethiopia. These refugee populations are very large. Nobody wants to receive them and there is little chance of them going back home.'

Refugees from famine and war are today being augmented by economic refugees. Economic conditions can produce movements of refugees that far exceed the movements that we have seen so far, says Tickell. Take the Vietnam trail. 'The Vietnamese have been leaving Vietnam in record numbers. The boat people have got on the high seas to Hong Kong and elsewhere. This problem is becoming virtually unmanageable. We've had to say to the government of Vietnam: you must change your economic policies to find employment and resources to keep people at home.'

In future, rising sea levels and changing climates will bring a new category of 'ecological refugees'. Tickell wonders: 'Is it going to be possible to resist this movement of refugees, of people looking for food and water and support and jobs and somewhere to put their families? Western Europe is a comfortable place where by and large things work pretty well. Yet if there were a big, big influx of refugees, would we be able to resist that influx on humanitarian grounds? And would you be able physically to resist them coming in? The USA cannot prevent the Mexican population from pouring across the frontier, even now. If things were to get as bad as they could get, it is going to be very difficult for those areas of the world that have hitherto resisted refugees to continue doing so.'

Mexicans swimming the Rio Grande is a popular American nightmare. But Alan Robock offers another scenario. 'Imagine 50 years from now, there's mass migration across the USA border. But they're not Mexicans coming into the USA, they are Americans going north into Canada, where they can grow food once deserts have replaced our farmland. I think that's a very extreme scenario, but its not out of the realm of possibility.'

Tickell believes that in many places the disruption caused by large influxes of refugees will bring escalating ecological destruction. He compares the neighbouring African countries of Zimbabwe and Mozambique. In Mozambique civil war has caused chaos. There is tremendous degradation of the environment. The trees are being cut down, causing soil erosion. And there is famine, says Tickell. In Zimbabwe 'a rural electricity programme is bringing cheap electricity, so people no longer cut down all the trees for firewood. They are enabling the environment to survive and prosper. But the arrival of more refugees from over the border in Mozambique would make it very difficult for them.'

The UN's Environment Programme is investigating these socio-economic consequences of global warming. Noel Brown at the UNEP lists Canada, Australia and perhaps Argentina and Brazil as countries with plenty of spare land that 'may have to be prepared to accept more people'. But few believe that the ordered planning and priorities of a UN agency will determine where refugees move if catastrophe strikes. If the precedents of Ethiopia and Vietnam are anything to go by, it is rather more likely that the UN's refugees agency will hastily be airfreighting tents, food and medicine to wherever the refugees run to as drought strikes or the seas invade.

PART FOUR

Prognosis for the Planet

CHAPTER 1

Technical fixes

Wally Broecker likes to take a detached view of the human predicament. 'If I were an observer somewhere in our galaxy watching planets, the most interesting period in the history of any planet that had developed a complex life system, such as we have on Earth, would be when one species takes over the planet—develops a civilisation, starts to pollute the planet, overpopulates the planet and threatens many other species. Today, on Earth, all these things are happening at once. I would say the Earth, after 4.5 billion years, is entering a narrow window of one or maybe two centuries when there is a transition from natural controls to man taking over the environment. Man has somehow to take the responsibility of managing the planet. The question is: will we wreck it before we get round to doing our job responsibly and becoming planetary managers?'

Broecker thinks that humans have gone too far to step backwards, to usher nature back to centre stage. There are too many of us and we have done too much damage. We have no choice but to take the controls of spaceship Earth. That may mean that conventional environmental thinking, based on leaving nature alone as much as possible, may have to go out of the window. We must, says Broecker, 'take the time to understand the basic elements of this system: what controls the cloudiness of our planet, how the ocean systems work, how waters are stored in soils and transmitted back to the atmosphere by plants—many basic things that we know something about, but really do not understand well enough to be prepared for the future.'

The logical consequence of humans taking charge of the planet is that we may have to intervene in radical and unexpected ways to mimic the work of nature. While looking at ways that nature influences the atmosphere, Broecker considers volcanoes. We know that they can cool the planet by several tenths of a degree. From Krakatoa a century ago to El Chichon in the 1980s, the evidence is clear. Now, as the planet warms, this trick of cooling the planet would be a useful one for humans to learn. Volcanoes cool the Earth because, when they erupt, they blast into the stratosphere vast amounts of very fine particles, mostly sulphate particles, that are extremely efficient at reflecting the sun's heat back into space. 'I think we should be prepared to consider steps like filling the atmosphere with sulphate particles,' says Broecker. 'We could have fleets of jets flying in the sky releasing this dust.' Broecker has done some sums. He reckons that a fleet of 700 jumbo jets could distribute 35 million tonnes of sulphate each year at an annual cost of around $10 billion. That would both cool the planet and give us lots of red sunsets of the kind that have fascinated artists after major volcanic eruptions.

There are other possible 'technical fixes'. One suggestion is to paint highways and the roofs of houses white, so as to reflect more of the sun's rays, or to cover the world's oceans with white polystyrene chips. Russian scientists have suggested putting into space giant reflectors to deflect sunlight before it hits the atmosphere. Broeker says that a doubling of carbon dioxide in the air—which is expected within 50 years—is the equivalent of turning up the power of the sun by 2 per cent. So covering 2 per cent of the sky should do the trick. Broecker calls this 'one grand and glorious and incredibly expensive engineering project'.

To most scientists such talk reeks of mad boffins experimenting on the planet. But Stephen Schneider is prepared to consider such ideas. After all, he says, technology got us into this mess, so maybe technology can get us out of it. High-flying aircraft spraying sulphate might work. 'They might actually scatter sunlight away. But we have a problem—the substantial uncertainty in our ability to forecast the effect. The climate system is incredibly complex and we're not up to forecasting the consequences.'

Suppose, says Schneider, that we make a mistake. Suppose that scientists overestimate the greenhouse effect—that it's not going to be 4° warmer in 50 years time, it's going to be 2° warmer. And suppose, in addition, that they make a mistake in assessing how effective the dust will be at cooling the planet. They could put up dust that they believe will cool the planet by 4° but it actually cools it by 8°. If the greenhouse warming turned out to be only 2° they could (with a chance of perhaps one in four) land up with a planet 6° colder than they started with. 'That would certainly be a cure worse than the disease,' says Schneider. 'And even if we were lucky and got it right, just imagine a small group of nations going round trying to modify the climate and we end up, right after the experiment, with a Sahelian drought or a Bangladeshi flood or a massive heatwave such as we had in the USA in 1988. It could be just by chance, an accident of nature, but immediately the victims would blame the modifiers of the climate for having done it. Our political institutions are nowhere near ready for that kind of engineering as a counter measure to the greenhouse effect.'

Alan Robock puts another fly in Broecker's ointment. 'What if all of a sudden the engineering project breaks down, or some political crisis means that you cannot do it any more for a year or two? The temperature would zoom up, we'd get warm much more rapidly. It would be as if you unplugged your refrigerator. What would happen to the food inside? The reaction would be extreme.' Mick Kelly has even less time for such notions. 'I think it's actually quite irresponsible to suggest that kind of approach,' he says. 'It's a surefire way of jumping from the frying pan into the fire.'

A less unpredictable response would be to extract carbon dioxide from the chimneys of power stations before it reaches the atmosphere. This would not solve the whole problem of the greenhouse effect. Power stations round the world are only responsible for around 30 per cent of carbon dioxide emissions due to human activity and around 15 per cent of all the greenhouse gases. But it would be a start, a logical step after the removal of smoke from power station emissions, which was largely completed in the 1950s, and the removal of sulphur, which causes acid rain, in most countries in the 1980s.

But the cost of 'decarbonisation' would be high. Carbon dioxide makes up more than 10 per cent of most power-station emissions: more than 1.5 billion tonnes of carbon goes up their chimneys every year. And the extraction processes themselves, which admittedly have not been developed much beyond the laboratory scale, use so much electricity that the first need would be for a lot more power stations to run the decarbonisation plant. Then the carbon dioxide has to be disposed of somewhere. An American researcher, Meyer Steinberg of the Brookhaven National Laboratory, has suggested liquifying it and burying it in old mines or abandoned oil wells. But the most likely option would be the bottom of the ocean, which, as Schneider points out, 'is where it all ends up anyway, except that if you put it into the air it takes a couple of centuries to get there'.

Steinberg's plan is to collect all the carbon dioxide from all the power stations, liquify it, and send it along giant pipes to the coast and out over the continental shelves until it can be dumped into the ocean depths. Beyond a certain depth, and so beyond a certain pressure, liquid carbon dioxide is more dense than water and will sink to the ocean bottom. There, the hope is, it will remain buried for ever. In Europe, the continent's carbon dioxide could go to Gibraltar where, not far offshore, the continental shelf ends and ocean currents flowing out of the Mediterranean would obligingly help the carbon dioxide down to the ocean bottom.

'It sounds like a good idea until you do the economics,' says Schneider. 'It would at least double the cost of producing energy from conventional fossil fuels. The costs would probably be prohibitive.' Most other investigators, including Steinberg, agree that unless there is a major technological breakthrough that makes the process radically cheaper, decarbonisation is not a serious option.

Kicking the coal habit

The single biggest source of greenhouse gases is coal. It is the main source of electricity round the world and responsible for no less than 80 per cent of the output of British power stations. Coal produces slightly more carbon dioxide for each unit of power produced than oil, and roughly twice as much as natural gas. Sir Crispin Tickell says: 'It's obvious that to build an economy on the use of coal is liable to produce a great deal of carbon dioxide.' The answer is to 'use something like natural gas or look into alternative technologies like solar power, or hydrogen power for vehicles, or of course go back to nuclear power.'

The case for acting now is strong, says Tickell. 'People can make decisions now

Mick Kelly, of the Climatic Research Unit at the University of East Anglia, believes that a global food crisis could be no more than a decade away.

In this Greenhouse Age, scientists have come to believe that Britain's dependence on coal must end.

which will yield results perhaps 20 years ahead with very important consequences for carbon dioxide emissions to the atmosphere.' He adds: 'Whether they want to do that now I cannot tell you. Some governments are more persuaded than others.'

The British government's stance is confusing. Margaret Thatcher has been second to no world leader in voicing her concern about the greenhouse effect and the duty of the world to hand on the 'leasehold' on our planet in a state in which we would choose to find it, with its life-support systems intact. Yet the Department of Energy, the branch of Whitehall that should be most intimately concerned with taking the decisions that Tickell wants to see, spent the first half of 1989 telling committees of both the House of Commons and Lords, who were investigating the greenhouse effect, that it was too early to act. Precipitate change might damage the national economy and, in any case, scientists had not yet shown that it was necessary, the department said.

Tickell continues: 'There are certain governments, in particular China and India and to some extent the Soviet Union, that are heavily dependent on coal and that have looked to their energy-generating future in terms of coal. They may need persuasion, but you find that already these governments are taking more account of international opinion. By far the most difficult one is China, but I doubt if the Chinese would wish to pursue energy policies over the long term which would create an effect which would be damaging to China, which is after all a large part of the Earth's surface. Maybe that is an optimistic view. Certainly we haven't persuaded the governments of China or India yet to change their public investment policies, but then what governments have we persuaded?'

What should be the priorities for future government investment policies? Tickell sees a rundown in reliance on coal as the major priority. But some scientists take a more radical approach. Mick Kelly says, 'The fundamental cause of the greenhouse effect is the waste, the over-consumption, the misplaced priorities that characterise modern-day society. We could cut by about 50 per cent the amount of energy each person uses in the industrialised world without any loss of standards of living. The fact that we've taken a development path which has meant that we have neglected that type of consideration is why we face the greenhouse problem. Waste and inefficiency really are at the root of the problem. We just have to be rather more sensible, rather more rational about the way in which we use resources.'

Stephen Schneider echoes a widely held view that most efforts at energy efficiency would make economic sense, regardless of the need to clean up our planet. 'More efficient power plants and better designed manufacturing processes would mean that the energy component of the cost of those manufactured goods goes down, pollution goes down and ultimately the countries that are wise enough to invest in efficient manufacturing processes will be more competitive.' The Japanese are the perfect example, he says. Their manufacturing processes are three times more efficient than those in the USA. 'It is part of the reason why we are being massacred by them economically. They are able to manufacture products cheaper.'

Meyer Steinberg, who considers that 'decarbonisation' is the mug's route to tackling the greenhouse effect, has conducted a study of the potential for energy efficiency in power stations, factories, homes, offices and vehicles round the world in the next 60 years. He has found that, using existing technologies, energy consumption could be cut by 60 per cent. The capital cost for the whole world would be a mind-boggling $24 trillion, but for most of the work there would be a good return on investment.

Friends of the Earth in Britain has been calling for recycling and an efficient use of resources since the early 1970s, when it made headlines by returning Schweppes non-returnable bottles to the company's headquarters to highlight its demand that the bottles should be recycled. Charles Secrett from the organisation presented evidence to a parliamentary committee in 1989 showing that existing technologies should allow Britain to reduce electricity demand by 70 per cent within the next 30 years. 'What we need is a government actually implementing those sorts of policies rather than building more power stations,' he says.

British electricity generating bodies are required by statute to generate and sell electricity. This they do with great skill. But, says Secrett, 'we don't actually have a demand for electricity as such; we have a demand for the services that electricity provides. We like to live in well-lit, comfortable buildings. We like the convenience of modern electrical appliances and we need electricity for industry. What we have to work out is what is the most efficient way of providing those services. What is the cheapest way, the safest way and the way that causes the least environmental impact. The answer is to use electricity more efficiently.'

Secrett wants much tougher building standards on insulation, for instance: 'If we were to have well-insulated buildings in Britain in the same way that they do in Sweden, we could save electricity that would be equivalent to ten nuclear power stations.'

Another campaigning point is the humble lightbulb. If you substitute the current incandescent bulb—typically a 75-watt bulb—with an equally bright long-lasting 18-watt fluorescent bulb, you are saving about 170 kilograms in weight of coal that would have to be burned over the lifetime of a bulb, says Secrett. 'You also save the person who is buying the bulb about £10 because they are using less electricity. The technology exists; it's just a question of putting the technology into place.'

Robock is also enthusiastic about the prospects for energy saving in the home. About a quarter of the energy consumed in the USA goes on lighting, heating and cooling buildings, all of which could be done much more efficiently, he says. 'It's possible to make a refrigerator that uses about 10 per cent of the energy that we use now, by insulating it better and by having a more efficient motor.'

Is this a cue for the green consumer to step forward and save the planet? Could an ecologically literate population, exercising its power in the market place, clean up the planet without the intervention of governments? Certainly the British government would prefer to do things this way. But Robock believes that change requires government action. The current cheapness of energy is a serious problem.

But governments can give incentives to manufacturers and consumers to use energy much more efficiently. 'That will be better in the long run for everybody. It will increase a country's economic potential because it will allow industry to develop technology which it can sell round the world, because soon everybody will have to be using this technology.'

While energy efficiency in the home can be achieved without a change of lifestyle, the American male might face some damage to his machismo out on the streets. The hundreds of millions of vehicles in the world today contribute at least a third of the carbon dioxide produced by fossil fuel burning. 'In the USA,' says Robock, 'it's American to have your own car and take your car when you go somewhere. You don't get on the bus or take a train.' But 50 people in 50 cars use a lot more energy than if they all sat on a bus. 'There need to be government incentives to use public transportation. We can lower the fare on the Metro. Washington DC is talking right now about raising the fare for the subway system. What message does that give the people? It tells them that we don't want you to ride the Metro. It would be cheaper for you to drive your car.'

The American attachment to the automobile goes further. 'Gasoline' in the USA costs about a dollar a gallon, a third to a quarter of what it costs in Europe where, partly as a result, people drive smaller cars and drive them less far. 'The only place where gasoline is cheaper than in the USA is next to an oil well in Saudi Arabia or Venezuela,' says Robock. 'If the government put a tax on gasoline it would be in everybody's interests. It would be part of an insurance policy to make the climate change more slowly. There are economic interests against that, people who make automobiles or tyres, or the oil industry. They have to be forced to change or to be given an incentive to change.'

CHAPTER 2

The nuclear hijack

Nuclear power 'to beat global warming'

United Nations, the World Meteorological Organisation and the World Climate Programme needed strengthening.

Agreement was also reached that a lead had to be taken to convince the developing world through aid and international institutions like the World Bank of the need for changes in energy policies and to promote afforestation.

Ministers present were Mrs Thatcher; Sir Geoffrey Howe, Foreign Secretary; Mr Ridley, Environment Secretary; Lord Young, Trade and Industry Sec-

the houses which will be around in 2020 are already built.

A public information campaign was needed to draw attention to the energy-consumption of appliances used in industry and the home and there could be benefits for industry in leading the world in energy efficient technologies.

Nuclear power also faced problems of public acceptance which needed to be addressed. There was agreement that there was a need to boost public confidence in nuclear power which could be the most environmentally friendly form of power generation, as it created no carbon

For the British government the nuclear option is the most attractive response to the greenhouse effect. When Margaret Thatcher held a teach-in on the greenhouse effect for ministers and officials in April 1989, scientists who had addressed the meeting emerged afterwards happy. They had been given an extensive hearing by the half-dozen members of the Cabinet present, they said. But they were angry the next day to discover that ministers must have been asleep much of the time—or had given misleading briefings to the press.

The story in the papers the following morning was, in the words of the *Daily Telegraph*'s front page headline, 'Nuclear power to beat global warming'. That wasn't what they had said at all, the scientists complained. Nuclear power was just one of a number of options discussed at the meeting, ranging from wind and solar power to energy efficiency. Indeed, the Prime Minister's press spokesman, Bernard Ingham, had specifically denied to a briefing of journalists after the meeting that nuclear power had been singled out for special approval. But clearly ministers (and the suspicion rested most firmly on Cecil Parkinson, the energy secretary) put a different 'spin' on the proceedings. The scientists felt that their meeting had been hijacked by the pro-nuclear cause.

Ironically, only a few days before the meeting, the government's UK Atomic Energy Authority had published in its monthly journal, *Atom*, an assessment of the role that nuclear power might play in stemming the greenhouse warming. The argument had already been given by the authority in evidence to a House of Commons select committee the month before. The authority concluded that just 11 per cent of the 'greenhouse gases' was produced by electricity; that that figure was therefore the maximum contribution that nuclear power could for the moment make to solving the greenhouse problem. 'The more efficient use of energy is the first essential step in tackling the greenhouse effect,' the authority said.

The truth is that, apart from a broad assault on energy efficiency, no single change, and certainly not nuclear power, can have more than a marginal effect on the greenhouse. The problem is too large and all-pervasive for that.

None the less, the nuclear option remains near the top of the political agenda, especially in Britain. Hard-pressed nuclear agencies and companies see it as their salvation, their chance to break free of the public opprobrium that has seen new orders almost dry up since the accident at Three Mile Island in the USA in 1979 and the Chernobyl disaster of 1986. In May 1989, British Nuclear Fuels ran a series of two-page advertisements in the national press on the theme: 'The Greenhouse Effect; We Have Part of the Solution.'

Tickell, is cautious. 'In scientific terms, the most important thing about nuclear power is that it does not create greenhouse gases. There are well-known problems associated with nuclear power, which were highlighted by the Chernobyl disaster, and people have perhaps been unduly worried by it. I think one has to realise that the problems of nuclear power are very largely problems which are soluble.' He says that these, include the disposal of nuclear waste.

Tickell denies that governments have a 'wild attachment' to nuclear power, asserting that it is 'a reasonable way of generating energy for the future. 'However,' he says, 'I don't feel very strongly in either direction. Let's see what happens.'

The anti-nuclear faction among scientists engaged in the greenhouse debate is unexpectedly strong. Many see nuclear power as part of a wider problem of man's environmental assaults on the planet, rather than part of the solution to the greenhouse problem. Alan Robock, for instance, says that the problems of nuclear waste 'may be environmentally more dangerous than the greenhouse warming'. Hubert Lamb, too, sees 'no solution in sight' for the problems of waste disposal.

Secrett from Friends of the Earth is an obvious opponent of nuclear power, but he puts the case well. 'At first sight and superficially,' he says, 'nuclear power seems attractive. But it is expensive, it is dangerous and it also produces its own nasty waste material that nobody has figured out a publicly acceptable or safe way of disposing of.'

A study conducted in the USA in 1988 by Bill Keepin at the Rocky Mountain Institute in Colorado concluded that measures to improve energy efficiency would be seven times more cost-effective than substituting nuclear power to reduce emissions of carbon dioxide from power stations.

Even if money were no object and public objections about safety were cast aside, there is a more basic difficulty about initiating a major programme of building nuclear power stations. The task would be just too big. Nuclear power stations are extremely expensive to build, though relatively cheap to run. The USA, according to some estimates, might need 8000 large nuclear power plants at a total cost of $750 billion to replace coal and oil-burning stations. Moreover, nuclear power stations take around a decade to design and build, and they require large numbers of people with highly specialised skills. Even a crash programme of training to provide the thousands of engineers and scientists able to handle such a task would take several years. And who would teach the teachers?

For Secrett, 'global warming is happening too rapidly and nuclear power is too expensive and takes too long to bring on stream to be able to contribute significantly to reducing greenhouse gases.' The nuclear option is, he says, 'a pipe dream that is simply not worth pursuing in the short term'.

As a self-confessed member of the 'Woodstock generation', an idealist who grew up in the 1960s, Stephen Schneider might be expected to oppose nuclear power outright. Instead, he opposes ideologues on both sides. He criticises the safety record of the nuclear power business and its supply of plutonium for nuclear weapons. But he also attacks environmentalists who 'absolutely refuse to utter the dreaded word "nuclear"', simply because it is associated with these misdemeanours. 'I think the attitude should be to welcome rather than to be suspicious' of a nuclear industry that has cleaned up its act. 'We should take a look at what they're saying and make sure that their specific plans are consistent with an environmentally sustainable development into the future. I worry most about ideology which says there is no compromise, because that kind of rigidity is almost certain to lead to political conflict in which the environment will probably be the loser.'

Nuclear waste and the next ice age

At the Climatic Research Unit, Jean Palutikof is working on a contract for Nirex, the British government agency in charge of disposing of civilian nuclear waste. She explains: 'Nirex is interested in safe disposal. They want to isolate the radioisotopes from the human environment for as long as they can be considered dangerous to people—for 1 million or 10 million years in the future.'

Nirex has asked Palutikof to look at the potential for climatic changes that might threaten the integrity of nuclear waste dumps over the next million years. 'You can't be very precise, obviously. You can only give them a best guess based on the current state of knowledge,' she says. 'There are a number of aspects of the climatic environment which could be dangerous on these timescales. The most obvious is an ice age. If you get glaciers rolling across the top of your waste repository, then it's possible in the worst case that they may strip all the cover off and that your repository will be exposed. So when people move back into the area after the ice age has retreated, they will be exposed directly to the isotopes.'

Palutikof has been looking at the timing of the changes in the Earth's orbit that might cause future ice ages. She has assessed the likely effect of a severe little ice age, which could bring tundra-like conditions to parts of Britain within a couple of hundred years, and of the kinds of subtropical climates that could be visited on us by the greenhouse effect.

The most recent ice age covered Britain to a line joining the Severn and the Thames. 'So anywhere north of that line you have to take account of possible ice age incursions.' The timing is also important. A nuclear dump will be much more radioactive in its first few thousand years. 'We're in fact overdue for a new ice age,' Palutikof says. The current interglacial period is already longer than normal. But we could have a wait of 60 000 years before the next glacial era. None the less, says Palutikof, 'In terms of the half-lives of the radioisotopes, that isn't so long as we might hope.'

'The one thing that Nirex can't take into account is how people are going to be living in the future. 'They assume that the future population will live in a broadly similar way technologically as people do today,' says Palutikof, 'but when you consider how far we've come in the last two or three thousand years, and if we're looking at 50 000, 500 000 or even a million years ahead, who can say what kind of changes may have occurred?'

Nirex try to take a practical approach to these problems. They build pessimistic assumptions into their calculations and install several lines of defence for the early years of disposal. Nirex will package waste in drums, but they don't package them in such a way that they are impermeable.' Nirex assumes that the drums will leak and corrode after a few years. They also assume that after 100 years all the plans and bits of paper that would tell future generations of the presence of the dump will be lost.

The next line of defence is a concrete bunker. 'But they don't expect that to last more than about 500 years. After that, they assume that the natural characteristics of the repository environment will impede the movement of the radionuclides. So they will attempt to site the repository in such an area that the geology, the groundwater and the climate will all impede the movement of the radionuclides once the material in which they are stored has decayed.'

Palutikof believes that changes in sea level pose the greatest threat to the kind of nuclear dump that Nirex have in mind for Britain, probably at Sellafield on the Cumbrian coast, or Dounreay on the rocky northern coast of Scotland. She believes that a drop in sea level is a more dangerous prospect than a rise—at any rate once the repository is full and sealed. While the greenhouse effect is causing the sea level to rise, an ice age would cause sea levels to fall substantially.

Her reason for fearing a fall in sea levels is that once a repository leaks, radioactive material, probably dissolved in groundwater, will start to move through rocks. At coastal sites, such as those proposed by Nirex, this movement will tend to be towards the sea. Radioactive material 'may well become exposed along the sea bed'.

Nirex may build their repository in shafts sunk beneath the sea bed from a coastal site. The idea is to ensure that any leakage will end up on the sea bottom rather than in somebody's field. The assumption is that there won't be anybody living on the sea bed. But that assumes that the sea continues to cover the area above the dump. 'If the sea level falls, and the area where the radionuclides have reached the surface is exposed, then the new land could be quite fertile,' says Palutikof, 'and you would expect people to move in and start farming. Your radionuclides could enter the food chain in concentrations that would be quite dangerous for human beings.' She calls this 'one of the most dangerous scenarios that you can envisage'.

Britain, she says, 'really isn't a very good environment for the disposal of nuclear waste. It is geologically varied; it is an island and quite vulnerable to changes in sea level; and being quite near the pole, we would expect it to become glaciated in an ice age.'

There may be two other options. One has been proposed by Secrett and his colleagues at Friends of the Earth. They say that 'since we don't know what's going to happen on these geological timescales, it is much more sensible to have on-site storage of the waste. If we're going to be subjected to another ice age, we would need to have those materials on hand to be able to remove them and take them to a place where they wouldn't be causing problems.'

The second option is not to impose on future generations the custody of vast waste stores. According to this line of thought, we should dispose safely of our waste in such a way that there is no chance of it troubling anybody ever again. Palutikof considers that the ideal burial ground is the Laurentian Shield, the great block of granite that covers most of eastern Canada. 'You have very, very old rocks where you really wouldn't expect any changes to take place. You could dig a very big hole, drop your waste and cover it up. The rock is very hard, so you wouldn't expect it to be stripped off by glaciers, even in an ice age. It is a long way from the sea and because the soils on top are not very fertile, you wouldn't expect a lot of people to move in there.'

But for the moment Britain is planning to dump its waste in geologically very variable rock, close to the sea in a place where farmers are likely to remain at work on fertile soils, and where an ice age is almost certain to rip away soils.

CHAPTER 3

Power to the people

If fossil fuels are out, and nuclear power is too risky, are "reversable" sources of energy the answer? About a fifth of the officially audited energy needs of the world are already met by some form of renewable energy. The main contributor is hydroelectric power. But renewable is not necessarily the same as ecologically sound. Fierce argument about the environmental acceptability of large hydroelectric schemes has raged in green circles through the 1980s. The British journal *The Ecologist*, edited by the environmentalist, Teddy Goldsmith, has conducted a virulent campaign highlighting the social and environmental costs of large dams. Goldsmith has railed against the 'lure' of cheap power offered by hydroelectric schemes. But people such as Secrett from Friends of the Earth argue that hydroelectric power 'is a very well-established, safe and proven way of producing cheap electricity'. The 'bad environmental and human impact can be dealt with through adequate management programmes.'

The argument extends far beyond the cloistered circles of British environmentalists. Hungary angered its neighbours Austria and Czechoslovakia in 1989, when it suspended work on a project to dam the Danube because of environmental concerns. China is engaged in a major internal debate about whether to go ahead with plans to dam the Yangtze River at a place called Three Gorges upstream from Wuhan. Concern for the many thousands of people who would be flooded from their homes and fears that the reservoir will silt up are tempered by the thought that Three Gorges is exactly the kind of billion-dollar investment in renewable energy that could prise China away from reliance on coal. Similar arguments surround two large dams proposed for the Narmada river valley in India, another country wedded to a coal-based future.

At heart, *The Ecologist* and its supporters believe that all economic development is bad for the world. The idea of 'sustainable development', the buzz-phrase of the late 1980s in many environmental and development circles, is anathema to them. They say that development is of itself not sustainable. As one column in the journal recently put it: 'In a finite ecologically connected world, belief in sustainable economic growth is no different from a belief in perpetual motion.' For many of those people seeking a way through the minefield of policy decisions created by the greenhouse effect, the task is to prove such pessimism wrong.

The oldest source of energy is fire. And today, away from the cities, the burning of dead wood and trees (now known in development circles as 'biomass') remains a prime source of energy for most people in most poor countries. You might not know it, however, since it rarely turns up in international statistics but biomass accounts for roughly 10 per cent of global energy consumption. The urban poor once relied on wood brought in by traders from the surrounding countryside. But in most places the trees have now gone and kerosene burns in the houses of the urban poor in the Third World.

Biomass contains carbon in the same way as does its fossilised remains, coal and oil. But it emits only about half as much carbon dioxide into the air. There is a long-running argument about whether the rural poor of the Third World should be 'wired up' for electricity or should get round the wood shortage by planting more biomass to burn for themselves. Tickell argues that the supply of electricity to town and country alike in the Third World is essential for 'ecological progress'. In Zimbabwe, he says, the supply of electricity has saved trees and helped halt the soil erosion that often follows the axe. When he was permanent secretary of the British Overseas Development Administration in the early 1980s, Tickell helped to provide funding for such projects.

But environmentalists such as Secrett and many aid charities encourage biomass burning, which they nurture with schemes to encourage people to plant trees. They regard biomass as a cheaper and more reliable source of energy than electricity for the rural poor of the Third World. It would also unleash less carbon dioxide into the air than burning coal in power stations to supply electricity.

The merits of energy from biomass are likely to be debated with increasing vigour in the coming years. Early in 1989 the US government's Environmental Protection Agency argued, in a study on how to beat the greenhouse effect, that biomass should be developed as an alternative fuel source for the rich world as well as the poor. The idea is not to bring back the wood stove (though that is the height of chic in many communities). The EPA says that 'current and emerging technologies could vastly improve the efficiency of biomass use [including] con-verting biomass to gaseous and liquid fuels and electricity'. Biomass in this context could mean things besides firewood. Both the EPA and the European Commission have investigated converting surplus grain into feedstock for gas-driven turbines, for instance.

An early development in the new greenhouse-conscious world is likely to be a switch to burning various fuels that contain carbon but emit less carbon dioxide than coal or oil. Natural gas will be prominent, especially in Europe where pipelines from Siberia are transporting vast amounts of gas into both eastern and western Europe, and where the North Sea is another provider. Natural gas, which is largely methane, produces about half as much carbon dioxide as coal and oil. Britain's first large gas-fired power stations are likely to be in operation by the early 1990s, though they are being built for economic rather than environmental reasons.

Burning natural gas may not be as beneficial as some assume. Some American investigators believe that pipelines carrying the gas leak up to 10 per cent of their contents. Since unburnt methane is a greenhouse gas, the pipelines may be a growing source of global warming as may gas vented from some oil fields. Another source of methane is rubbish dumps. A recent study by the Open University calculated that more than 2 million tonnes of methane seeps from British tips each year. One estimate of the global total is 70 million tonnes. Sometimes the methane is lethal. In March 1986 a bungalow at Loscoe in Derbyshire was reduced to rubble when methane from a nearby rubbish tip seeped into the basement and exploded.

Methane from some tips is collected by pipes buried in the waste and taken to nearby factories where it is burnt in boilers. This is nothing more than a rather advanced use of biomass to create energy. The waste tip becomes a convenient method of converting biomass into gas. It could kill two greenhouse birds with one stone. Methane could be kept from reaching the atmosphere, and instead could substitute for coal in producing electricity or heat.

The problem for all clean sources of power is that their dirty competitors do not have to pay the true cost of their dirtiness. The widespread damage to humans and the environment caused by conventional fuels such as nuclear power and coal and oil, is not costed into the price of the fuels. The bill is borne by the community at large. For instance, neither the British nor German electricity generators have had to pay the damage, costing many billions of pounds, that they have done over many decades to Scandinavian fisheries, German forests or British cathedrals. Noel Brown at the UN Environment Programme says that electricity generators have run up vast 'earth debts'. These debts are just as real as the cash debts incurred by many poor nations in recent years—and far less likely to be paid back. Had those 'earth debts' been written into the debit side of their balance sheets, the electricity generators might long ago have invested in renewable sources of energy.

That is why many scientists and policy makers now argue for a 'greenhouse tax' on the burning of carbon-based fuels. It would be a way of using conventional measures for controlling free-market economies to impose the real cost of energy generation.

What about nuclear fusion the power that fuels the sun? In early 1989, scientists in Utah claimed that they had perfected nuclear fusion, in a test tube at room temperatures. Controversy raged as to whether it was true—or a blunder of misinterpreted data. If true, it appears to open up the prospect of cheap, clean energy for all. Even cars, perhaps, could run on small fusion reactors.

Hyperbole ran riot. And at the height of it, Palutikof, having argued the case for planting wind machines across our hillsides, accepted that 'everything I have said could be turned completely upside down by the invention of cheap nuclear fusion. We may not need wind power. Perhaps there is really going to be some glorious tomorrow when all our problems will be solved. Let's suppose that it is safe, that it is cheap, that all it needs is sea water. Then all our concerns about energy will be over. At present, this nation and the world are spending an awful lot of money on energy-related issues, all of which, so far as one can tell, would disappear if we had cheap nuclear fusion. It would free us to worry about other issues. We could really begin to throw a lot of money at things like agricultural research, for instance.'

Charles Secrett was not so keen to be carried away. Whatever the truth about cold fusion, he said, 'We cannot turn test-tube experiments into practical operating experience in the timescales necessary to deal with global warming. We have to start combating global warming right now. We have the technologies available to do it. Hypothetical solutions distract us from the real task in hand.'

Winds of change

The Dutch knew a thing or two when they covered their countryside with windmills. Soon, Britain too could be resorting to wind power as one solution for the greenhouse problem. We could also pipe waste heat from power stations to heat homes and offices, and fuel small power plants with methane, tapped from putrefying refuse tips before it has a chance to join the other greenhouse gases in the sky. Many of these 'alternative' sources of energy have been on the drawing board and in small prototype machines for many years. But they have been allowed to languish, while the British nuclear industry has been able to call on whatever resources it has needed to keep its atomic fires burning.

Wind energy should have a special attraction for Britain. We live on the west coast of a continent, in middle latitudes, where strong winds constantly buffet our coasts. We are on the receiving end of the northern hemisphere's equivalent of the roaring forties. Palutikof says that 'the only other part of the world that really is a better place for wind energy is New Zealand.' So why not allow the wind to turn the blades of wind turbines? Some researchers believe that 30 per cent of Britain's electricity could come one day from wind power. Even a reluctant Department of Energy admits that wind is the most promising of the available alternative sources of energy, and is close to economic viability.

Britain already has a handful of small wind machines, in the Orkney Islands, Caernarvon and Kent. 'All of them are rated at 330 kilowatts,' says Palutikof, 'which means that they'd run 330 one-bar electric fires if they were running as fast as they could.' That is hardly a flying start, but the Central Electricity Generating Board has announced plans for three wind farms, collections of wind machines. One will be in the north Pennines, one in west Wales and a third in southwest England. Each farm will have 25 machines and should join the national grid in 1992, with a total capacity of about 25 megawatts.

Wind power may be greenhouse-friendly, but it does have its handicaps. 'They foul up our view, make a noise, keep you awake at night and interfere with your television set,' says Palutikof. They also have a habit of pitching javelin-like blades into your front garden.

A large 'workhorse' wind machine, of the kind that researchers expect to see in action in Britain before the 1990s are out, will have blades about 10 metres

Windmills powered
Holland for centuries.
New, high-tech
turbines may bring a
return of windpower.

long. You would need 2000 or more of these to produce the amount of power generated by a typical nuclear or coal-fired power station. These machines have to be at least 200 metres apart in order to harvest the wind efficiently. Wind power, concludes Palutikof, is 'very, very wasteful of space and it could disrupt an awful lot of people'. To replace a nuclear power plant such as Sizewell, you would need to cover an area the size of Greater Manchester with wind turbines.

In a country generating its electricity from wind power 'almost everybody would have a wind turbine in their backyard'—rather like the Dutch and their windmills, in fact. That is why many advocates of wind power see the future in farms of large wind generators moored offshore. The world's first offshore turbine is about to be built 18 kilometres off Wells in Norfolk. In future, turbines may be assembled on top of abandoned North Sea oil platforms, a nice symbol of the decline of fossil fuels and the arrival of the 'renewables'. 'People who like to look a long way into the future,' says Palutikof, 'have this vision of wind turbines across the North Sea, with individual turbines up to 100 metres across and generating perhaps 10 megawatts each. But we're a long way from the technology to do that.'

The solution to winding down the world's reliance on fossil fuels is likely to vary round the world. In Britain and northern European countries, including West Germany, the winds may form part of the answer. But wind power would be useless in most of the tropics, where solar energy is a much better bet. It's horses for courses. Though New Zealand is windy, it may prefer to stick with hydroelectric power, which it has in abundance. Geothermal energy in the form of hot rocks or hot water in the bowels of the earth is a possibility in a few places in Britain: Cornwall and Durham have so far been investigated. But France might be better occupied exploring its large geothermal resources rather than putting all its eggs into the nuclear basket.

Most investigators believe that a lot of these technologies need time to develop. And meanwhile, the most urgent task for the world is to learn and apply the art of energy saving in all its forms and in every corner of the globe.

CHAPTER 4

Answers in the soil

An early priority for the world, as it takes stock of the menace from the greenhouse effect, is to call a halt to the rampant destruction of rainforests. Brazil, which engaged in an extraordinary orgy of destruction in the late 1980s, is under intense pressure to do so. Early in 1989 Thailand heeded the clamour of complaint and ended the destruction of its rainforests, except where replanting would take place. Other nations in the Far East, such as the Philippines, Malaysia and Indonesia, may follow suit.

There should also be calls to replant the world with trees. In many countries outside the tropics new forests are being planted—albeit usually with serried ranks of pine trees rather than the oak and ash of the former woodlands. From South Korea to New England, more trees are being planted than destroyed. This replanting is now making a substantial contribution to minimising the overall loss of carbon dioxide from the world's forests. But much more could be done. One estimate is that if an area of the planet the size of the continental USA were planted with fast-growing varieties of trees, this could absorb as much carbon dioxide as is currently being emitted from burning coal and oil. 'Global plantations' could grow in countries with spare land. If nothing else, this would give the planet a few years' breathing space from the greenhouse effect.

The attraction of the idea is that, from the day that the first tree is planted, it will be doing good (and doing it visibly). But there are snags. Once the trees are fully grown, they will no longer suck carbon dioxide from the air. They must then be harvested, their wood put into permanent storage, and replaced with new saplings. It would not be easy to decide where to plant all these trees, nor who should pay. Perhaps nations should be told to balance their carbon 'budgets', paying through a greenhouse tax for the planting of forests to soak up the excess carbon dioxide that they put into the atmosphere. According to this rule West Germany would have to plant more trees than it could fit on to its entire 250 000 square kilometres. Who would provide a home for Germany's trees? Might Britain have to accept, for the global good, more trees covering even more of its moorlands and Scottish highlands, the only large empty expanses left in a crowded country?

Most people would agree with Pat Zimmerman who says that 'a reforestation programme is important in terms of slowing down the increase of carbon dioxide for a certain period of time. But it can't work in the long run, over more than 100 or 200 years.' Sir Crispin Tickell thinks that replanting may become part of the world response to the carbon dioxide element of the greenhouse effect. But what about the other elements? The problem of CFCs is being addressed because of the ozone hole. But how could an agreement be framed on limiting emissions of methane, the second biggest cause of greenhouses warming, and the fastest growing?

Tickell, like many investigators, believes that in the long run, methane may prove a more technically intractable problem than carbon dioxide. 'Whereas you can begin to see ways in which you could diminish the quantity of carbon dioxide in the atmosphere, so far we've not been able to pinpoint and understand exactly how methane works. No one knows exactly where the extra methane is coming from. It may be coming from tundra, which is warming up. It's certainly coming from animals. But what is certain is that it is increasing greatly.'

Richard Warrick says that if the extra methane comes mainly from cattle and paddy fields we have a difficult problem. 'It is hard to see,' he says, 'how we can possibly cut back on that production in a world in which we have an expanding population and the need to increase world food production, particularly in the rice-growing regions.' All cows produce methane, though modern breeds of cattle may produce less methane and more meat. There are greater hopes for a breakthrough in rice cultivation. If rice does not need to be grown under water in paddy fields, then the oxygen-free conditions in which methane-producing bacteria get to work could be banished. One reason for flooding paddy fields is to prevent weeds from taking over the fields. So it may be possible to grow rice without covering the plants in water, if another way can be found to stop the weeds, perhaps by chemicals or by developing genetically stronger rice plants.

Noel Brown says that the cultivation of 'dry rice' may be possible. 'There are a number of companies that are advanced in biotechnology and genetic engineering and we are talking to them to see if they might look at a genetically engineered rice strain that might help us,' he says. Within a few decades, the replacement of paddys with fields of new strains of dry rice could become a major feature of the world's efforts to rid itself of the greenhouse problem.

We cannot stop the tundra melting and releasing fossilised methane without halting global warming itself. But we could drain the world's bogs and end the production of methane in 'marsh gas'. Global warming may help by making some places drier than they are today. But other places will become wetter so that overall there will be an increase in the world's bogs.

A ban on large-scale forest burning will stem an important source of methane in the air as well as carbon dioxide and nitrous oxide. But real progress to defuse the 'timebomb' of the build-up of nitrous oxide in the air probably depends on reducing the world's dependence on nitrogen fertilisers. The action of soil bacteria on these compounds may unleash large amounts of nitrous oxide into the atmosphere. And output could soar over the coming decades as the use of nitrogen fertilisers increases in the developing world.

Charles Secrett points out that the rich nations remain the biggest users of nitrogen fertilisers. There may be conflicts in the future, he argues, between the need to produce more food in poor countries and the desire to reduce emissions of nitrous oxide. The solution, Secrett hopes, will lie in technology. 'In developed countries, which have very intensive agricultures, it is possible to continue growing the food that we need and use much less fertiliser. This is because we can apply it more efficiently to fields. We can put it on to fields in a way that guarantees a much greater take-up of the nutrients by the crops themselves.' The difficulty comes with the poor nations. 'There nitrogen fertiliser is used in much smaller quantities, yet the Third World is where the population explosion is going to occur. Undoubtedly those countries will have to use nitrogen-based fertilisers to increase food production. I don't think that people in the West are going to be able to tell the Third World that they cannot feed their people because of the problem of global warming.' The challenge in the Third World, he says, is going to be how to develop agricultural systems that use less nitrogen fertilisers.

Thirty years ago there were widespread fears that the world's farmers would not be able to keep up with the expected doubling of world population. They succeeded, however, largely through the development of improved crops such as rice that thrive on the application of nitrogen-based fertilisers and the defence systems provided by pesticides. Crop yields soared. 'But now,' says Secrett, 'we're faced with a different sort of problem. I don't think it's beyond human ingenuity to work out the answer. The secret undoubtedly will lie in crop breeding programmes. In the same way that we've developed crops that respond to high chemical inputs with high yields, so we now have to develop staple and luxury food crops that respond in a different way, that can guarantee high yields without needing massive inputs of fertilisers and other agricultural chemicals. It is a technical problem. I think it can be resolved, but it will take time and the people who most need food should not be the people who pay the penalties.'

CHAPTER 5

Crying wolf

'The atmosphere knows no boundaries; the winds do not carry passports.' With these words Sir Crispin Tickell proposed in May 1989 that the nations of the world should draw up a convention on climate change, a global agreement to tackle the greenhouse effect. British ministers dressed the idea up as their own, but in reality it had been under discussion since the previous summer when Malta submitted a proposal for action by the UN.

There was innocent sport in the spectacle of British ministers responding in a slightly bemused fashion to their prime minister's wish for them to be seen to be busy tackling the greenhouse issue. However, Tickell is genuinely a leading figure at the UN in bringing the issue before the councils of the world. He is credited with masterminding Thatcher's conversion to the cause, causing many whispered queries about his powers of persuasion. After spending most of the 1980s as a reforming permanent secretary of Britain's Overseas Development Administration, he may now emerge in the 1990s as a lynchpin of the efforts to save the planet from climatic catastrophe.

He sees 1988 as 'the great turning point' in the task he outlined more than a decade ago. 'In that year, all people became conscious of the greenhouse problem in a way that they had not before. As ambassador to the UN, it was interesting for me to see the way in which this was picked up by that well-known debating society, the UN General Assembly.' The assembly gave its blessing to the Intergovernmental Panel on Climate Change, a scientific committee set up by two UN agencies, the UN Environment Programme and the World Meteorological Organisation. The committee is to report to a World Climate Conference in 1990 on what will happen to the world in response to the greenhouse effect, and what can be done to stop it. The advice is likely to form the basis for specific international action—for example banning the destruction of rainforests and setting targets for reducing emissions of carbon dioxide—under the convention on climate change proposed by Britain.

During 1988 and 1989, says Tickell, 'a lot of governments have been thinking about how best to treat the problem of greenhouse gases in a global fashion.' There was a major speech on global problems from Mikhail Gorbachev at the UN in November 1988, in which he stressed the threat from climatic change. Some European heads of government met in The Hague in March 1989 to call for a new international body to enforce a 'law of the atmosphere', imposing sanctions on countries that do not toe the line. Tickell, along with Thatcher, who refused to attend the meeting in The Hague, is critical. 'Working in international institutions as I now do makes me rather sceptical of this idea.' Such bodies, he says, 'are extremely hard to invent. They take a terribly long time.' He backs the use of existing institutions, whether the UN Environment Programme or the UN Security Council to co-ordinate international action.

'I think the important thing at the moment is that the intergovernment panel should meet, should have the full support of those participating and should come up with a scientific base.' Britain is again taking an important role, with a working group on the science of the greenhouse effect, based at the Meteorological Office in Bracknell and chaired by the Office's director, John Houghton.

Tickell, more than most, must be impatient at the delay in getting under way action that he knows (indeed knew a decade ago) needs to be taken. The government, for all its headline grabbing, is as yet committed to doing nothing. Measures to cut carbon dioxide emissions are 'a long, long way off', said Environment Secretary Nicholas Ridley in May 1989. Tickell responds diplomatically: 'In the case of the greenhouse effect, yes, the rate of change is extremely worrying. We ought to be doing something about it, but I think myself, and I really say this very solemnly, it would be a great mistake to ask governments to launch actions and above all adapt investment programmes unless they are already convinced on the basis of good scientific evidence. You have to reduce uncertainties to an acceptable level. At present I don't think that is fully the case.'

His great fear is that too much scientific uncertainty will cause negotiations for a clean-up to go off half-cock, that a valuable chance for action may be lost and progress against the greenhouse effect may be put back many years. 'There is a great danger that people will cry wolf, as has happened in the past, and then nothing happens,' he says.

Many people point to the successes of negotiations to cut emissions of CFCs and save the ozone layer as a model of how global action on global warming could come about. Tickell points rather to the 'famous case' of the failure to take such action in the early 1970s, when warnings that the ozone layer might be under threat were first made. 'Too many claims were made' for the results of the first scientific work—some of which turned out to be erroneous. 'It was, for example, suggested that the use of supersonic aircraft might be destroying the ozone layer.' This turned out to be false and for a while, says Tickell, the whole idea of a threat to the ozone layer was discredited. 'The result of everyone crying wolf too soon was that when we actually came down to dealing with the very real problems of the ozone layer there was a certain amount of scepticism.'

Tickell fears that the same story may be repeated after the claims made in the summer of 1988 to the US Congress. Then, at the height of a major drought, James Hansen, a leading American climate modeller, claimed that the drought was due to the greenhouse effect. This claim grabbed headlines round the world and led directly to the 'great turning point' that Tickell saw in the greenhouse debate. But was it good science? Soon afterwards, Hansen published a paper on work done on his climate model at NASA, which predicted more droughts in the USA during the 1990s as a direct consequence of the greenhouse effect. But that is a long way from attributing a particular cause to a particular drought. Climatologists studying weather maps a few months later concluded that the prime immediate cause of the drought had been the 'La Niña' ocean current then washing across the Pacific. Ironically, 'La Niña' was cooling most of the planet.

Such a refutation of Hansen's specific claims could turn the whole greenhouse debate in the USA into a 'few-day wonder', says Tickell. If the planet cools for the next two or three years (as appeared to be happening in 1989) and the rains return to the American Midwest (which seemed less likely, but given the workings of chance is bound to happen at some stage) then the international impetus could dry up as fast as the prairies green again.

Schneider worries less about the problems of crying wolf. Of Hansen's dramatic claims of June 1988 he says: 'People have a lot of trouble relating to something as seemingly theoretical as the greenhouse effect. They need some metaphor in their own experience.' He thinks that the US drought or other events in 1988 such as Hurricane Gilbert and the September floods in Bangladesh do meet that need for a metaphor. Do such events prove the greenhouse effect? 'Well, as much as I'd like to say it does, it really doesn't.' The climate is in many ways random. Schneider uses the example of throwing dice. If the USA throws a few hot years it could just be bad luck. It will be a long time before it becomes clear whether or not the dice have been loaded by the greenhouse effect. 'We have to let nature roll its climatic dice for the next several decades to find out if we've loaded them.'

But there's a risk, he says. 'It's not cost-free to wait 20 years to find out if the warming to date has been caused by the greenhouse effect. The price is that we will have to adapt to a much larger dose of change than if we try to do something about it now. And that's a social dilemma, not a scientific dilemma. It's a trade-off which says: Do we fear most the possibility of rapid climatic change coming without trying to slow it down? Or do we fear most making an investment now, even though there is a possibility it might not be as bad as the scientists say? There is no scientific way to choose that. It is up to the public to decide how they want to gamble with the future of their own planet.'

Secrett picks up Schneider's point. He believes the public will decide. Ultimately, if Thatcher, Bush, Mitterrand, Kohl and the rest of the world leaders pick up the greenhouse gauntlet it will be because their voters insist. But will the voters insist? 'In our armchair, TV-dominated culture, the tendency is for individuals to sit back and say, "Oh, God, what can I do? There's nothing. I may be very concerned about these problems but they're all happening at such a global level that it has to be the responsibility of governments or of other people to solve." I don't have much sympathy for that view, because there's a lot that individuals do that actually helps cause the problems in the first place.

'One of the easiest things for people living in Britain to do is to make sure that

Charles Secrett, from the Friends of the Earth (above left), believes that a Green approach could stave off the Greenhouse Effect. Tom Wigley of the Climatic Research Unit at the University of East Anglia (above right) is also an optimist.

Mikhail Gorbachev, at the UN in December 1988, joined the call for a global initiative, to tackle our changing climate.

Margaret Thatcher called a conference to discuss the thinning of the ozone layer in March 1989. She demanded that developing nations join the fight, but many, such as China and India, pinned the blame on the rich world.

SAVING THE
OZONE LAYER
LONDON
CONFERENCE

they use as little electricity as possible; to make sure that their homes are well insulated and when they buy electrical appliances to always buy the one that is the most efficient. When the individual action is multiplied a thousand or millionfold, as it can so easily be, then one can have a real tidal wave for positive change, building up through the activity of individuals.'

This has happened in the past, says Secrett. Public opposition forced the removal of aerosols containing CFCs from supermarket shelves years before the deadline set by the UN's Montreal Protocol for 1999. 'The attitudes of government and industry towards CFCs changed almost overnight as a result of thousands and then tens and hundreds of thousands of people all over Britain saying it's crazy to buy aerosols that contain these chemicals.' Public interest in how individuals could help the environment has turned *The Green Consumer Guide* into a bestselling book in Britain, selling 220 000 copies in its first eight months on sale.

But for many environmentalists there is a downside to green consumerism. They see it being used by free market economists and their right-wing political supporters to argue that political action is unnecessary. The Department of the Environment in Britain is proud to say that the nation has met the terms of the Montreal Protocol without any law being passed or any threat of legal action. And the Department of Energy has argued that energy saving is in the interests of individual firms and householders, so the department has no need even to increase its own research.

Secrett's former boss as director of Friends of the Earth in Britain, Jonathon Porritt, has warned of the dangers of green consumerism. But Secrett says that green consumers can be just as powerful in the political market place as in the supermarket. They can and will force governments to act directly to save our environment. 'Even very large global problems like the greenhouse effect can be solved because industry and governments, who are primarily the people responsible for developing the appropriate policies, sit up and take notice. Election times are very good opportunities to do that.' Secrett was speaking weeks before the Green Party's astonishing success in the elections to the European Parliament in May, 1989, made his case for him.

2020 vision

Secrett was speaking weeks before the Green Party's astonishing success in the elections to the European Parliament in mid-1989 made his case for him. Such an approach may be less successful in parts of the world where personal day-to-day survival dominates the lives of most people. This emerged clearly at Mrs Thatcher's ozone conference in March 1989. She had hoped to persuade large developing nations, notably Brazil, India and China, that they should sign the Montreal Protocol and work to cut their emissions of CFCs. She met a blank wall. As Secrett puts it, those nations 'made it absolutely clear that they were not about to sacrifice the opportunities that are coming to them for the first time to accelerate their economic progress just because there seems to be a problem like the ozone hole or global warming looming on the horizon.'

Delegations from both China and India told the meeting that any problem from CFCs to date was the rich world's doing. The rich world had grown rich on exploiting cheap sources of energy, such as coal, and cheap refrigerants, such as CFCs. So if the rich world now wanted the poor world to take a different and more expensive road to prosperity, then the rich world should foot the bill. In the phrase of Noel Brown from the UNEP, the rich world should pay back its 'earth debt'.

Nations such as China, which have huge supplies of coal within their borders, and Brazil and Zaire, with their rainforests, could one day hold the future of the greenhouse effect in their hands. They may be able to extract a considerable price for their co-operation. But they are also the straws that could break the planet's back.

Imagine that in, say, 2020 the world is in crisis. Emissions of greenhouse gases from Asian coal-fired power plants soar; floods in Bangladesh drown millions and the grain fields of the USA dry to a frazzle. The world might be pleading with governments in Beijing and New Delhi to change tack. But the majority of the carbon dioxide in the atmosphere on that date would still have come from Europe and North America, pumped there mostly during the second half of the twentieth century.

As the world's leaders begin to address ways of meeting the greenhouse threat, they will have to grapple with this fact, and with the aspirations of the developing countries to better themselves. There is the ever-present possibility of a backlash in the poor world against the claims of scientists in the rich world, who always seem to conspire against their economic development. Panos is a progressive and independent organisation based in London but partly funded by several Scandinavian governments. It is devoted to spreading news and views about development and the environment from Third World countries and prides itself on having a finger on the pulse of the developing world. It chose the occasion of the Thatcher ozone conference to publicise the views of one of the Third World's more prominent environmentalists, Gurmit Singh, the president of the Environmental Protection Society of Malaysia. Rather than highlighting the threat to our planet posed by chemicals that destroy the ozone layer, Singh instead asked, 'Why this ozone scare?' He claimed the many governments of poor nations, including Malaysia, were signing the Montreal Protocol to restrict CFCs out of a fear that trade sanctions would follow if they did not. 'There is hardly any scientific evidence to show that ozone depletion is yet a significant problem over any single developing country,' he said. In a fascinating echo of the days when Stalin claimed that there was no such thing as socialist pollution, Singh said: 'Genuine people participation will certainly allow the evolution of ozone-friendly products.'

Noel Brown, as a Jamaican working for the UNEP, can see better than most the risks posed by such thinking. 'There's a growing apprehension,' he says, 'on the part of a number of developing countries that suddenly they are going to be identified as the principal causes of the global warming. For a number of years it was the population boom that had been the principal issue. Then in the 1970s, the principal economic gospel was limits to growth, and many developing countries became very suspicious of the entire environmental movement. Some saw it as another imperialist trick to deny us our right to pollution, because pollution meant progress. Now it's deforestation, and countries like Brazil are becoming extremely nervous that the exploitation of their forest resources may now be projected as a major contributor to global warming. This could trigger a backlash on the part of many developing countries who, in trying to break out of the vicious cycle of poverty, are seen to be creators of great environmental harm.'

Brown contrasts the USA's desire to exploit the oil reserves of Alaska with Brazil's desire to exploit its own natural resource—the trees of the Amazon rainforest. Both will add to the greenhouse problem. But while Brazil's plans face fierce international rebuke, the USA's oil plans escape criticism. 'We have to avoid ecological double standards and name-calling,' says Brown.

Workineh Degefu says that 'the majority of developing countries don't feel they are part of the greenhouse problem. And they don't feel that it will affect them.' That could change, he states, if African scientists for instance are able to do their own research into the possible effects of climatic change on their continent. But even so, 'it is very difficult to ask developing countries to stop deforestation ... unless a cheaper substitution for energy which will be easily available to the poor countries is introduced. It may take time before the developing countries can stop utilising their forest resources and coal resources for energy in particular.'

Secrett believes that 'the rich industrialised countries must provide the money and the technology that will allow developing countries to pursue a different path of economic progress that can still provide their citizens with material comforts, but without repeating the environmental mistakes that countries like Britain and America made when we were pursuing our path of industrial progress.' The sharing of new energy-efficient technologies will be a real test of how co-operative global warming solutions are going to be put into effect.

CHAPTER 6

The real world

In this political quagmire, Tickell believes that the realities of the environment in the tropics must intervene. 'There is a terrible tendency,' he says, 'to think that every country in the world can follow the same pattern of economic progress as those in the temperate lands.' This idea is flawed, he maintains, because the environment in the tropics, where most of the world's poor live, is very different from that of the rich temperate lands.

The temperate lands will stand much more physical abuse than most of the tropics without sliding into ecological disaster. The fact that this is unfair makes it no less true. 'Temperate areas have rain, resources and the ability to do things to their environment which they can later repair, because kindly nature has so arranged things. But there are other countries where this is not the case, where if you damage the environment you damage it for ever.' In Africa, he says, the soils are generally very hard and acidic, the rainfall is only spasmodic and the prospects for growth are not the same as those in the temperate lands. 'I think that's a very basic geographic fact.'

In political terms, this sounds like a kind of ecological imperialism. But Tickell sees a hint of a diplomatic breakthrough. If his geography is correct then he can argue that poor nations have no alternative but to take a new, less polluting road to economic development. He can appeal to self-interest rather than international good neighbourliness.

The acid test, as usual, is China. At present, says Tickell, China's future energy strategy 'is very heavily tilted towards coal because coal is what they've got. But there are a lot of other ways of generating energy in China. And if the Chinese, who are extremely intelligent people, come to the conclusion that the use of coal is damaging themselves as well as the rest of the world, they are going to look for alternative technologies. It is the responsibility of the existing industrial countries, who have created the problems, to try to find the kind of technologies which can help the world generate energy in an acceptable global fashion'.

Tickell says that he was persuaded of this belief when at the Overseas Development Administration. 'I used to go to countries all over the world to talk about their economic plans. It is not difficult, when the facts are known, to persuade a country that its path towards greater prosperity lies in one direction rather than another—that the destruction of forests is going to hurt that country and that short-term solutions are unlikely to be the best ones.'

Not everybody shares this harmonious vision in which we all have the same interests and reason prevails. Many see the need for a cruder deal to rescue the tropical rainforests, for instance, from the chainsaws and fire lighters. One popular idea is 'debt for nature' swaps. Many Third World nations are crippled by debts owed to the world's bankers. The debts are the product of profligate lending policies adopted by many of the banks in the 1970s and early 1980s, when they were awash with 'petrodollars' invested by oil-producing nations when oil prices rocketed. Few banks expect to see their money again, but many are unwilling to write the debts off. Environmental groups such as the World Wide Fund for Nature (formerly the World Wildlife Fund) have pioneered the idea of buying the debts at their market value, which is low because of the small prospect of eventual payment. In debt for nature swaps, the debtor nations continue to pay the interest on the debt, but in their local currency and in the form of expenditure on conservation. Environmental groups arranged several deals of that sort in 1988 and 1989 with Latin American governments such as Bolivia, Ecuador and Costa Rica.

But the big catch, Brazil, with a debt burden of more than $100 billion and the pressing problem of the destruction of the Amazon rainforest, eluded them.

Ghillean Prance finds his desire to conserve the rainforest sucking him into discussion about international finance. 'The international debt is so great in these countries,' he says, 'that their economies are in chaos. I think the only way we can really help them to be able to afford conservation and proper research on sustainable systems is by debt forgiveness.'

The first 'debt for nature' swap was in Bolivia. The government there has extended a national park and is investing to conserve it properly. In Costa Rica, the Guanacaste National Park was set up in July 1989 after the purchase of $24.5 million of foreign debt in a deal involving the Swedish International Development Agency. In return for the termination of the debt, the central bank of Costa Rica provided $17 million in government bonds to fund part of the cost of establishing and maintaining an 80 000-hectare park in the northwest of the country, including the 'ecological and biocultural restoration' of parts of the park already damaged by human activities.

It is a start, agrees Prance, but 'we need much more global measures of debt forgiveness.' In mid-1989, the world's banks remained cautious about setting up swaps involving tens of billions rather than tens of millions of dollars. And Brazil remained distinctly cool to the idea of 'debt for nature' swaps. Antonio Magalhaes, State Secretary of Ceara State, Brazil, called the idea 'nonsense' because 'it does not solve the environmental problem or the debt problem. What Brazil needs now is the capacity to finance its own sustainable development that takes care of economic growth, of social equity and environmental protection.' He wants no deals with outside environmental agencies. Instead, 'we need to have a renegotiation of the debt.' Brazil believes that if the World Wide Fund for Nature can buy bits of Third World countries' foreign debt at knockdown prices, then so should the countries themselves. If Brazil could buy its debt for the market price, 'we could reduce our debt from \$150 billion to \$35–40 billion, and then the capacity of investing in Brazil would be recouped and the country could finance sustainable development, preserving the Amazon and the other fragile ecosystems of the country.'

In pursuit of this aim—and to get the world off its back—Brazil is preparing a plan for the sustainable development of the Amazon called 'Our Nature'. The plan was greeted sceptically. But at least it fits Tickell's view that the best long-term approach to global conservation is to persuade nations that such conservation also serves their own best interests.

Earth debt

At the end of June 1988 a meeting of scientists and policy makers in Toronto won headlines round the world for its call for a 20 per cent cut in emissions of carbon dioxide from all sources by the year 2005 and an eventual cut of 50 per cent. This bold call, coming at a time of growing awareness about the greenhouse effect, has since become the benchmark for discussions on responding to the threat. And so has its suggestion for a policy tool to achieve the task: a greenhouse or carbon tax.

Stephen Schneider of the National Center for Atmospheric Research says that a carbon tax will recognise the true cost of burning fossil fuels. Far from being an interference in the free market, he says, it will acknowledge failure of the existing economic system to put a proper price tag on the cost to the planet of polluting the air. It will embrace the principle that the polluter should pay for the cost of his pollution.

'The present market is not free,' says Schneider. 'It is rigged because coal, which is the worst polluter, and oil, the second, and natural gas, the third, are not being charged any price for the degradation of common resources, namely the environment and our climate upon which we depend. The market would be free if we accounted for the actual cost of the use of those fuels.' For example, says Schneider, the cost of burning fossil fuels should take account of the coming rise in sea levels and budget for the billions of dollars of territory that may be flooded as a result. 'We need to weight that into the price of doing business.'

The income from the tax should not be used to 'bail out politicians' but to retrain redundant miners, to provide income for poor people who will face higher energy prices and to pay for research into more efficient cars, homes and manufacturing processes. More money might also go to the World Bank, whose loans would be tied to projects to improve energy efficiency, such as better coal-fired power plants for the Chinese. 'The key to the Third World situation is not to preach about how to live, but to provide opportunities so that their own development can be more environmentally sustainable. If we are going to tell the Brazilians they cannot chop down virgin rainforest in the Amazon—that they cannot have the economic benefit from doing that—then we also have to say that we will provide loans so that the already deforested areas can become plantations for coffee or pineapples or whatever, so that they have alternative employment.' Schneider emphatically does not believe that either poor people or poor nations should be exempt from the carbon tax. Subsidising cheap fuel would encourage its profligate use—exactly what the world is trying to avoid.

Noel Brown looks at this tricky issue of equity in a different light. A means must be found, he says, to acknowledge that the rich world got rich by pouring greenhouse gases into the air. Most of that gas is still there, warming the planet. The rest is absorbed in the oceans, which as a result may one day lose their ability to absorb more. 'We have been talking about the Third World financial debt, but let's also talk about the "Earth debt" that the rich countries now owe to the rest of the world for past environmental misdemeanours that now threaten the planet.' Perhaps the world as a whole should be financially compensated for the damage. Certainly if the nations of the world begin to talk seriously about a carbon tax then some nations will want to work out the cumulative unpaid tax due from the developed nations for their economic development over the past 200 years.

Brown believes that the nations of the world must now view the 'ecological security' of the planet as a more potent threat to their survival than any threat to the security of their national borders. This idea was promulgated by Mikhail Gorbechev when he spoke to the UN General Assembly in late 1988. Unfortunately, the force of his words was lost when he rushed home shortly afterwards to attend to the aftermath of an earthquake in Armenia. But the Soviet idea of setting up an ecological security council provides a glimpse of the new scale of values emerging for the greenhouse world and suggests a key role for the UN in meeting the challenge. Perhaps the UN has at last found its true role.

Brown argues that changing ideas about security should bring changes in spending. 'A large percentage of the world's resources that have been earmarked for military protection may have to be transferred to ecological protection,' he says. An environmental lobby group in Washington, the Worldwatch Institute, recently compared the world's current spending on military defence with the likely cost of what it called a 'sustainable future budget'. Worldwide military spending is currently around a trillion dollars a year, while the planet might be saved on a budget of perhaps $150 billion a year.

Carl Sagan, the scientist who first publicised the idea that a freezing nuclear 'winter' would follow a nuclear war, has calculated that the Cold War of the past 40 years has cost $10 trillion. Brown says: 'I asked Carl what can you buy with $10 trillion? He said everything. Every boat, every factory, every farm, everything.'

For Brown the Cold War showed, among other things, that 'society is willing to make long-term investment of a significant magnitude in what it considers to be essential for its security. We need the same kind of investment now to ensure our survival on this planet. Let us say that we are engaged in a Cold War on behalf of the Earth and we need to make that kind of investment. Perhaps we will do it if we can see with the kind of immediacy and gravity that the other Cold War projected. Maybe the new slogan will be not "Rather dead than red" but "Rather green than dead." '

People of the Third World will bear the brunt of the changing climate. There could be more dust storms in Ethiopia.

Sand dunes threaten this village in Niger. Deserts may advance in the Greenhouse Age.

CHAPTER 7

Back from the brink

How should humanity face up to its new and terrifying responsibility to manage the planet and its ill-understood life-support systems? With hope. There is little to support the view of pessimists that somehow we are draining the resources of our planet in such a way that we are doomed. Moreover the technologies that could drag us back from the abyss are well known, if not yet fully developed. And the cash is there, too, though largely still in military coffers. So is the ingenuity. About half of all the scientists in the world work for the military. If all this creative energy and money were spent on helping to develop the world there would be plenty of resources to go round.

But will we do it? To start with, the world must realise that catastrophes can and do happen. The generation of politicians that will have to manage the green-house will be too young to remember the conflagration of the Second World War. Will that help or hinder them in understanding the altogether greater potential for disaster inherent in nature?

A sense of prehistory may help. Alan Robock would, take those leaders back 65 million years to 'a tremendous catastrophe, a mass extinction, when all the dino-saurs died—in fact when every animal bigger than a cat on the face of the Earth died.' The effect was an ecological nightmare. All the possible disasters were going on at once, with incredible intensity. The meteorite sent billions of tonnes of dust into the atmosphere, which cooled the planet, like a giant 'nuclear winter'. But so much carbon from limestone rocks may have been injected into the air that a greenhouse effect soon swung temperatures wildly upwards. And there could have been a 'super-acid' rainfall, too, caused by the formation of concentrated nitric acid as the meteorite, several tens of kilometres across, careered through the atmosphere. 'There were fires burning throughout the continents and a tremendous climatic catastrophe. This teaches us that there can be tremendous changes on a global scale,' says Robock.

The disaster paved the way for the rise of mammals, but it also saw off the dinosaurs, which had dominated the planet for tens of millions of years. That too offers us a lesson. 'Almost every species that has ever existed in the history of the earth has gone extinct, and there is no reason to think that our species won't go extinct one day,' says Robock. 'The question is: will we evolve into some superior being or will we ruin the place so that we can't exist and some lower animal will take over?'

The dinosaurs probably died for lack of food. They starved while smaller animals that were able to dig up roots could make enough energy for themselves to keep going until the climate returned to normal. Humans today have adapted their environment so that it can produce large amounts of food—much more than when we were hunters and gatherers. But the farming business is vulnerable because of its intensity, just as the dinosaurs were vulnerable because of their size.

'If we make the planet inhospitable through chemical pollution or by changing the climate or by destroying the ozone layer, then perhaps some other species which is more resistant to those things will become dominant,' says Robock. In a nuclear holocaust, for instance, insects can survive since they are extremely resistant to radioactivity. 'There'll be roaches around long after we've gone.'

Mick Kelly offers a Doomsday scenario. 'I believe that the impact of global warming could well be catastrophic. That crisis could occur within 20 years. It's not unrealistic to envision that within the next 10–15 years there will be a major decrease in crop yields in North America as the continent dries up and droughts hit the Midwest. This region is the bread basket of the world. It's at the moment supplying the major proportion of world food reserves available to countries that cannot grow their own food. If harvests are reduced in North America, if the world price of grain rises, then we would see mass starvation in the Third World. This could happen very quickly.'

Pat Zimmerman is gloomy about the world's chances of finding the political will to act early enough to stop some greenhouse crisis in a few decades' time. 'I'm not very optimistic that we're going to be able to halt emissions of greenhouse gases,' he says. 'I think that people will not be willing to make the hard social choices to head off this problem. The best we can hope for is to create a good research infrastructure. Then, in 10 or 20 years, when we really have to make these choices, when we don't have alternatives, we will be able to provide the scientific widsom to make good decisions. I think that is the most we can hope for.'

Many researchers see our fate as inextricably tied to halting the growth in the world's population. More people require more land and destroy more forests. They also burn more fuel and so contribute to the greenhouse effect through adding to the atmosphere's load of carbon dioxide and methane. There are more than 5 billion people on the planet. The rate of growth of population has begun to slow, having peaked in 1973, but the number of extra mouths to feed each year continues to rise. Demographers believe that the world's population will stabilise by the end of the twenty-first century, but not until it has reached around 10 billion people. Zimmerman says that 'in the long run our only hope is to try to control the growth of human population.' That will be the only way to stem the increased emissions of greenhouse gases. Other researchers believe that a more energy-efficient world, in which resources are properly managed, will be more easily achieved than attempting to halt population growth.

But, whatever their views about population growth, most scientists share Zimmerman's frustration about the slowness of politicians to act to halt climatic change. 'I'm frustrated,' he says, 'because the issues are known. We know how to do the research and people are talking about co-ordinating international efforts: they say funding is on the way, but it's going to be a year or so . . . I feel a bit like a guy who walks off the end of a pier with his pocket full of lead and people say don't worry, the tide goes out in an hour. We really don't have the time to wait. We need to get busy. We have to build teams of scientists. We have to think on longer timescales than 10 years or even 100 years.

'One thing that we can do is store a surplus of grain now. Grain will keep for a thousand years. We should take some of our agricultural surplus and save it, because it is going to take time to adapt to our new environment, to develop crops that will grow in places that will be hotter than today with different rainfall regimes. I think we have to think about hard questions, too, like whether there are too many people on earth. I wouldn't advocate that we eliminate people, but it is easier not to have them born than to watch them waste away.'

Ghillean Prance from Kew Gardens also believes that population is a fundamental issue. 'I don't think that the human species is necessarily doomed because we've dominated the earth. Surely, we're intelligent enough. The first thing to address is the expanding population and that we have to stabilise world population. If we can do that, if we can really address the population crisis, then we can live together with the environment, with the rest of the organisms. If we don't do that then we are doomed.'

Doomed? Tickell won't hear of it. He could even be suspected of looking forward to the future. 'I think one must be optimistic in thinking that mankind, having created a problem, will eventually be able to desist from action that makes it worse and eventually take actions which will make it better . . . It may take some time. I don't think any government is yet fully persuaded of the need to take countermeasures, but I don't think the ultimate end can be in doubt because it is in every country's self-interest.'

Another determined optimist is the weather man from Adelaide, Tom Wigley, who has turned climatic sage to prime ministers. 'Will man survive? Yes. Man has survived greater climatic changes in the past. He survived the last ice age, a much harsher time than we expect to occur in the future. It's harder to survive cold than it is to survive heat. But some parts of the world are certainly going to be very harshly affected by climatic change.

'In the industrialised countries we do not really have too many problems. Although it might be a very expensive process adapting to a rapidly changing climate, we have the resources to be able to do that. But the less developed countries have less scope for adaptation. They are living at the edge of sustainability right now, so any adverse change, whether towards higher temperatures or less rainfall or whatever, is going to be very hard to cope with.'

The most basic requirement is that we should be able to feed ourselves. Hence the horror of Mick Kelly's Doomsday scenario. However, Richard Warrick professes optimism about the world's ability to feed itself. The farms of the developed world will be able to adapt to drier climates, he says. 'It doesn't take all that long to develop new varieties of crops that would be better adapted—about 8–10 years for wheat'. Severe droughts have peppered the history of the American Midwest, most notoriously the dust bowl of the 1930s, which caused financial ruin to many farmers and triggered the population's migration west. But America has adapted since the 1930s. Subsequent droughts have not been so costly. Why? 'Farms are bigger now; crop varieties have changed; irrigation has spread; and there is now an underlying social safety net to protect people and farms from climatic extremes.'

On the other hand, in the developing countries there are already severe setbacks to agriculture during droughts or floods. The Sahel in Africa and Bangladesh in Asia are the prime examples. 'These areas are very vulnerable to climatic change,' says Warrick, because they do not have the technology to adapt or the wealth to provide a safety net for farmers in distress. 'Probably the most important thing for these countries to do to insulate themselves from climatic change is to increase their economic development.'

Technology, Warrick believes, offers the best chance of solving the world's problems, since it allows those able to afford it to adapt to a warming world. Should we rely on technology to see us through? Some environmentalists believe that technology is our downfall. We have little choice but to retrace our steps to a smaller, simpler world. But most environmentalists, like Secrett, argue that the need is to redirect our technology towards a new set of aims, towards an energy-efficient 'sustainable' economic development rather than profligate growth.

Stephen Schneider wonders about the possible technological breakthroughs: 'What about some new genetically engineered crop that will take advantage of the extra carbon dioxide? I think these kinds of technological solutions do offer a real opportunity in the future. The problem is that they are not guaranteed. Are we going to commit the entire future of the planet to the possibility of a technological fix that is not at all certain? My view is, let's solve problems through conventional means while making some small investments—like insurance premiums—in developing those alternative technologies. But to count on them is a major risk which I for one would not want to take with the planet.'

Schneider and Wigley are at heart optimists. Their beliefs have led them to take their science into political circles. They have no intention of sitting back in their laboratories moaning about how politicians are screwing up the world. They believe that there are solutions and they intend that the politicians should be both scared by the scale of the crisis facing the world and fully briefed on what to do about it.

Schneider believes that the world will have to roll with the climatic punches while it gets its house in order. 'I'm pessimistic that we'll be able to prevent some damage,' he says. 'Already we've built up greenhouse gases that have lifetimes in the atmosphere of decades or centuries. We cannot reverse that. And it is not possible for us to stop our dependence on fossil fuels in even a decade because that would be economically catastrophic.' He sees a more gradual adoption of more efficient uses of resources and then of renewable sources of energy. 'We are committed already to, let's say, at least 1° of warming and perhaps several within a few decades. This is very fast and there will be disruptions. On the other hand a 2° warming is not the same as 6°. And—I hate to say this because I don't want people to take too much comfort from it—we can take advantage of alternative climates, with longer growing seasons, for instance. We can take advantage of change if we know what it is in advance and if it comes slowly enough for us to adapt. Change can literally be extinction for those living at the margins, but if we can slow it down then we have more time to adapt. My optimism is that the greenhouse effect represents an opportunity for us to get our global development house in order. And if it scares us a little bit into doing the right thing on population, on improved standards of living for the poor and reduced waste for the rich, then it's worth it.'

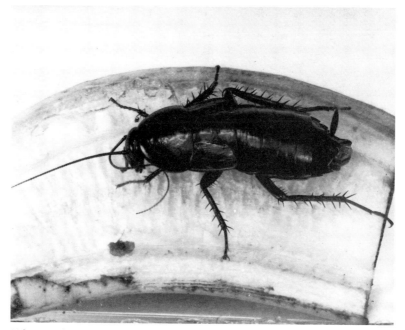

Whatever happens, scientists say that the cockroaches will survive. . . .

A Selected Bibliography

Climatic Change and World Affairs, Crispin Tickell, Oxford (1977)

Climates of Hunger, Reid Bryson & Thomas J. Murray, Wisconsin

Turning Up The Heat, Fred Pearce, London, (1989)

Weather, Climate and Human Affairs, Hubert Lamb, London, (1988)

The Little Ice Age, Jean Grove, London, (1988)

Drought and Hunger in Africa, Ed: Michael Glanz, Cambridge, (1987)

The Co-Evolution of Climate and Life, Stephen Schneider and Randi Londer, San Francisco, (1984)

A Matter of Degrees, Irving Mintzer, Washington, (1987)

The Greenhouse Effect, Stewart Boyle and John Ardill, London (1989)

The Ages of Gaia, Jim Lovelock, Oxford (1988)

The Greenhouse Effect: Climatic Change and Ecosystems, Bert Bolin et al, Vienna, (1986)

In The Rainforest, Catherine Caufield, London, (1985)

The Greening of Africa, Paul Harrison, London, (1986).

Picture Credits

Index

175